Smoky Mountain Tall Tales and Other Yarns That I Recall

Smoky Mountain Tall Tales

And Other Yarns That I Recall

Uncle Bud Beasley

Table of Contents

Forward

Chapter One
Smoky Mountain Yarns of Some Renown

Chapter 2
Tall Tales from the Lumberjack Camp

Chapter 3
Excerpts from the Bestseller "How to be a Lumberjack"

i

Chapter 4
Real True Personal Stories You Should Believe

Chapter 5
Odds and Ends

Prologue

Forward

Hello friends! My name is Uncle Bud Beasley. You didn't know you had an Uncle Bud did you? But you do.

For the past 20 years or so I have been living here in the Great Smoky Mountains, but my love of the area goes way back to my childhood. I was five years old when my parents bought our first little camper, a thirteen foot Scotty, and we began our camping adventures. Many summers were spent in the national forest, camping at Elkmont near Gatlinburg and over in North Carolina, at Smokemont, Balsam Mountain and Deep Creek.

As I got older, there were church youth trips to Gatlinburg, where a couple of dozen teenagers piled into a big old log cabin and slept on the floor or where ever we could find a space to lay out a sleeping bag. We'd walk up and down the streets of Gatlinburg, buying souvenirs for the folks back home, and take side trips over to Pigeon Forge, pre-Dollywood, which was far less busy than it is today.

When I got a family of my own we continued to visit the area, and I began to explore ways I could bring my skill set here and figure out a way to make a living in these mountains that I love. That opportunity came when I was 42 years old, when I became a cast member in a dinner theater here celebrating the history and heritage of these Great Smoky Mountains. Right smack dab up my alley. That show went away, but I'm still here.

After that show closed, I had the opportunity to work in a new dinner show that featured a lumberjack competition between the two best logging camps in the Smokies. Heck, I didn't even know there used to be a logging industry here! But that opportunity taught me how important the industry was to the development of the area, including introducing tourism to the Smokies. And gave me the chance to began to write songs and stories that celebrate this important part of American history.

This little book is a collection of stories and songs that I have written over the past dozen years or so, sharing with you not only my love of the Smokies, but also stories from my life before I moved here. They were written for me to tell out loud, in my very own way of speaking, so every word might not be grammatically perfect, but it's how I talk, so there. I have used the names of a few of my real, actual friends in some of these stories, but I changed the events to protect the innocent. Some of these stories are completely true, some are based in truth, and some I made up just for fun.

I'll let you decide which is which.

Chapter One

Smoky Mountain Yarns of Some Renown

Chopper and Sawyer

Back in 1975 I was 14 years old and had participated in a youth government program called "Boy's State." And through that association I was invited to spend the entire summer at a educational slash working camp up in the Smoky Mountains. This program was an off shoot of the old Civilian Conservation Corps that President Franklin Roosevelt started in the 1930's, and we lived in an old CCC camp about 15 miles in the mountains up from Cades Cove.

There were about 20 of us, boys and girls, and the camp consisted of a boys barracks, a girls barracks, a mess hall and the counselors cabin, which was considerably nicer than our accommodations. We were there to learn about conservation, and participate in several projects which turned out to be manual labor, clearing brush and picking up trash and what not from the hiking trails. You know it's amazing what folks throw on the ground on a hiking trail.

Anyways, the first night after we got settled in, we were all in the canteen after supper and they had brought in a genuine US Forest Ranger to do a little safety talk. He had this big board where he had samples of poison oak and poison ivy, and some pictures of some snakes, like rattlers and copperheads, and even had a real rattle that he shook so we could hear what death sounds like. And right there at the

1

end, he got to the main attraction, what we had all come to hear about, Ursus Americanus, the American Black Bear. Of course, most of us had seen bears before, and knew better than to approach one on purpose. We weren't exactly tenderfoots. All of us grew up camping and such. And we knew that bears didn't want to mess with us any more than we wanted to mess with them, and that if you did accidentally came across one, just stop and make some kind of noise and they would most likely move on.

The problem is people. Why folks think they need to pet a bear, or feed a bear, or for heaven's sake, take a picture of their kids with a bear, is beyond me. Bears are wild animals, and do just fine without your Little Debbie Snack Cake, until they've had a few and then they aren't so shy around people anymore and that's when there's trouble. Then they have to be tranquilized and relocated up in the mountains.

Two such bears had been relocated just a few miles up from where we were and they were well known around the camp. They even had names, Chopper and Sawyer. They were veterans of the relocation game, and had been moved up from Gatlinburg to the mountains every year for the past several years and were quite comfortable around people. You ever hear of a wild animal getting a taste for blood? Well these bears had a taste for peanut butter. Everything at the camp had to be locked up tight when Chopper and Sawyer was around.

Now we all took turns helping the camp cook Cookie in the mess hall, and this particular day was my turn. Everybody else was about a mile up the mountain clearing a little stream that had gotten clogged up, and long about lunchtime I set out with a knapsack full of sandwiches for them. I recon I was about three quarters of the way there when I came across Old Sawyer rooting in a dead tree stump. So I stop and

2

jingle the bells they gave me for just such and occasion, but Ol' Sawyer just looked up at me and sniffed in the air. So I jingle a little harder and holler at him a bit, but he's got that big nose up in the air and starts my way. So I start backing up. Now just so you know, you cannot out run a bear. A bear can get up to 30 or 40 miles per hour and you cannot. But I'm backing away and ringing those bells for all their worth and suddenly I hear a grunt come from behind me and I turn and there's Chopper. He ain't no more than 20 feet away and he's got his nose up and I'm between them.

There is this tree about ten feet to my left, so I decide to make for that tree. In three seconds flat I am up that tree about 15 feet or so sitting on this limb. And just so you know, bears can climb trees. But if the choice is between getting eaten on the ground or taking a chance up in a tree, choose the tree. So I'm up there trying to figure out what to do next and I remember all those sandwiches I got in that knapsack. I look down and Sawyer and Chopper are right there at the base of that tree and it won't be long before they start climbing, so I grab one of those sandwiches and toss it a little ways out from the tree. Well both them bears start right after it and Sawyer gets there first, so Chopper looks up at me and I toss him one a little further away.

This goes on for thirty minutes or so, with me throwing each sandwich further and further away, until I am out of sandwiches. By now the bears are about 100 feet from the tree, and I recon that's the best head start I'm going to get, so I start climbing down, and I hear a crack and next thing I know, I'm falling through the air. I hit the ground hard, and all my breath goes whoosh! Right out, and I must have hit my head pretty good, cause when I come to, I see two bears standing over me, looking down at me laying there on the ground. Chopper looks at Sawyer and looks back down at me and says, "Are you alright?"

Well I don't say nothing, cause I'm not used to a bear talking and all. And then Sawyer says, "You fell out of that tree. Are you OK?" Well to tell you the truth, I'm not sure whether I was OK or not. But they helped me sit up and I had some water in my canteen and they gave that to me and leaned me up against the tree. I was coming around a bit better, and starting to get my wits about me, when I noticed that Chopper was sitting next to me and Sawyer was *taking our picture,* then they changed places and Sawyer got his picture took. Then Sawyer said, "You got any more of them sandwiches?" I shook my head no, and he patted me on the shoulder, and they just sort of wandered off into the woods.

And that's how they found me, sitting on the ground leaned up against that tree with a couple dozen sandwich wrappers scattered around. I never did tell them the whole story, just enough to get by. And you may think I'm crazy or lying or maybe it was the fall that scrambled my brains. But somewhere high up in those mountains, there's a bear's den. And in that den I recon there are a couple of pictures of me and two peanut butter sandwich loving bears hanging on the wall.

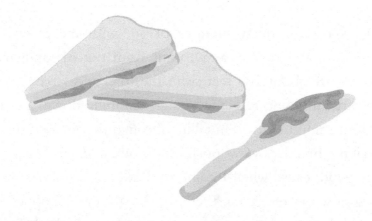

That's What A Bear Is Good For

When I was a boy and the world was small
I didn't have no use for bears at all
They're an ornery, thieving, no a count, dirty clan
But our old camp cook took me aside
And he said "Son I'll open your eyes,"
And show you how the bear can service man...

B is for bear bacon, to begin every day
E is eggs and bear meat, and bear claw etouffee
A is any bear part you can put into a stew
R's a rack of ribs this big and bear rump barbeque,
Sliced bear, spiced bear, deep fat fried bear, pickled bear and more
That's what a bear is good for!

B is for bear burgers, braised with bear steak tips
E is enchilada bear, bear salsa and bear chips
A is any bear part you can throw onto the grill
R's a roasted hunk of bear a most delicious meal
Broiled bear, boiled bear, wrapped in foil bear, bear toes by the score
That's what a bear is good for!

But a bear is good for more than just eating,
there's other things you can use a bear for...

B is for bear blankets to pile up on your bed
E is bear ear ear muffs, to warm your little head
A is any bear part you can render down for oil
R is for the bear skin rug, that decorates your floor
Put it all together and you'll find that you adore
All the things that a bear is good for!
Yo – Ho!

5

The New Medicine Man

In this next Great Smoky Mountain Tale, I'm going to take you back hundreds of years, back before the European settlers came to this land. When the only people here in the Smokies were the Cherokee. Now the Cherokee lived close to the mountains they called home. They hunted in the forest and fished in the rivers, and gave thanks to the great God Yo Ho Wah, who watched over them. And they were a wise people, far wiser than the explorers that came from across the ocean. As a matter of fact, we refer to these people as "Indians" and do you know why? When Ol' Christopher Columbus landed in North America, he thought he was in India! Anyways, at night the Cherokee would gather around the fire and sing songs and listen to the stories the old ones would tell.

Now each village had it's own Shaman, or medicine man, and they were considered the wisest and most powerful men in the community. They knew all about plants and how they could be used to heal the sick, they could speak the language of the animals and control the weather by talking directly to the wind and the rain. And some say they could work black magic, and had power over life and death.

7

It was in the spring, and the warm sun had melted the winter snow away and the blossoms shot forth from the tree branches and the mountain came alive once more. The wise old medicine man stood by the river and stared up at the first new moon. He knew it was time to pass his position on to a younger man. For the past seven years, he had trained four men in the traditional ceremonies of the people, in herbal medicine, in the ways of nature and even the dark art of enlisting the spirit world to intervene on their behalf. Now he must decide between the four, a decision as difficult as the importance of selecting correctly. And so, he created a test. A test to prove which one was the wisest and best to take over. He called the men before him and told them, "Deep in the mountains, a full day and night's journey from this village stands the tallest tree in the forest. At the base of that tree lies your test." The next day the men started out, each one certain that he would be the one to pass the test and become the leader of his people.

As the day turned into dusk, and the dusk became the night, they walked on, without speaking, each lost in his own thoughts. Finally as the dawn broke on a new day, they came to the tree. There, at the base of the tree, was a large pile of bones. The first man spoke, "These are strange bones! It must be our challenge to identify the animal they came from. I will reassemble them so I may see, and be the first to pass this test." And with that, he began to beat his drum.

Oh dark spirits! Hear my plea!
It is I the leader of the Cherokee!
I command you assemble this dry pile of bones
And reveal the creature to which they belonged
Oh dark spirits! Answer my call!
And prove that I am the wisest of all.

And the wind began to blow, and the ground began to shake, and slowly the bones began to come together, first the feet, then the legs and up and up, faster and faster, until at last there stood the skeleton of a huge black bear!

The second man laughed, "That was too easy, that cannot be our challenge! I will give the bear flesh and fur and teeth and claws as though it were alive!" And he began to beat his drum.

Oh dark spirits! Hear my plea!
It is I the leader of the Cherokee!
Cover these bones with flesh and hair
And bring forth the essence of this bear
Oh dark spirits! Answer my call!
And prove that I am the wisest of all.

And the wind began to blow and the ground began to shake, and flesh and fur began to appear around the bones, and the thick black fur soon covered the bones and the claws and fangs shimmered in the morning sun.

But the third man said, "These are only tricks. The real test is to bring the bear to life!" Now the fourth man had been listening and watching without saying a word, and when he heard this, he quietly began climbing the tree. The third man banged his drum,

Oh dark spirits! Hear my plea!
It is I the leader of the Cherokee!
I command you breathe life into this dead form
And make this bear reborn
Oh dark spirits! Answer my call!
And prove that I am the wisest of all!

But nothing happened! So he banged harder! "Oh dark spirits! Hear my plea!" Nope. Nothing. Nada. And so he took a deep breath and banged his drum louder than ever before, "Hear my plea!" And just then, the wind began to blow, and the ground began to shake, and a bolt of lightening came from the sky and the bear came to life and gobbled up the three men. Then he wandered off into the woods.

The fourth man climbed down from the tree and made his way home. When he arrived, he was greeted by the entire village and became their new medicine man for he truly was, the wisest of them all.

The Legend of Ranger Smoky Black

Smoky Black was born in a shack up in the middle of the wood
He was strong and bold barely ten years old
when he left that shack for good
It was in the fall when he heard the call to fight for his country
He took his gun and he whipped the Hun and kept America free
Ranger Smoky Black kept America free

Now after the war he returned once more to the mountains of his birth
He saw the need so he planted the seed to save his mother earth
Old Roosevelt knew just how he felt so made a declaration
Conserve this land for every man and woman in this nation
Ranger Smoky Black conserved the land
And kept America free

A pack of scouts on a field cook out wandered from the trail
As they roamed the park it was getting dark
and their flashlight started to fail
They were filled with fright as they lost the light and felt so all alone
But the scouts all cheered when he appeared and led them safely home
Ranger Smoky Black saved the scouts, conserved the land
And kept America free

It was hot and dry in mid-July in a far off mountain camp
'Neath a big pine tree campers carelessly dropped a kerosene lamp
The wind did blow and the fire did grow, burning up the land
But Ranger Black held the wild flames back
with his shovel and some sand
Ranger Smoky Black fought the fire, saved the scouts,
conserved the land,
And kept America free

On a hiking trip to the mountain tip a family crossed a bear
She was in the mood for the hikers food that she smelled in the air
As she attacked our Ranger Black swooped in to save the day
He shook his towel and with a might growl he chased that bear away
Ranger Smoky Black scared a bear, fought the fire,
saved the scouts, conserved the land,
And kept America free

Scared a bear with a mighty growl
Stopped a fire while the wind did howl
Saved the scouts in the dark of night
Conserved the land and did what's right
And kept America free!

Gatlin Hijacks the Burg

In 14 hundred and 92, Columbus discovered America. In 1620 the pilgrims landed at Plymouth Rock. In 1776, the British Colonies declared their independence. And in 1806, a woman named Martha founded Gatlinburg. Come close kids, and hear the my tale of the founding of Gatlinburg Tennessee.

Now all y'all know Gatlinburg as the Gateway to the Great Smoky Mountain National Park, a vacation destination for millions of folks. But back before 1800, the only people to vacation in the Gatlinburg area were Cherokee Indians. Alright. Vacation might not be the right word. Passed through might be more accurate.

And in 1801, a farmer from South Carolina named William Ogle, came through and he decided to make the area his home. When he first laid eyes on the flats surrounded by steep mountains, he believed he had found "The Land of Paradise." With the help of the Cherokee, he chopped down some trees and notched the logs to build a cabin. He piled those logs up and then headed back home to farm one more season, to get him a store up to help him and his family settle in. Now he had planned on moving his family the following year, but unfortunately, he caught the malaria and died in 1803. His widow, Martha Husky Ogle, got all broke up and so she moved the family to Virginia where she had some kin. Now this could have been the end of the story, but Martha was made of fairly hearty stock. And sometime around 1806, she got to itching to see the land her dead husband had went on and on about. So she got to telling the stories to her daughter and her husband, and a fore long she talked them right into making the long haul across the mountains. It was Martha, her daughter and her husband, who were McCarters, and her brother Peter Husky. When they got here, they found the logs left by 'ol William and put together the very first permanent home around these parts over near Baskins Creek. As their families grew, the area became known as White Oak Flats.

Things went along pretty quiet for a while, but after the war of 1812, the US gave former soldiers 50 acre tracts of land for their service, and we had us a population explosion. The Regans, Ownbys, Whaleys and Bohannans all moved in and soon there was the makings of a town.

So you may be wondering how did White Oak Flats become Gatlinburg? Well long about 1854 this feller named Radford Gatlin moved in from Georgia and opened up a general store and established the first post office. By all accounts, 'ol Radford was a rascal. He was kind of an egotistical religious nut, a jack legged preacher so to speak, and when the local Baptist Church didn't suit him, he formed his own church called it "Gatlinite Baptist Church." That did not sit well with most folks. They thought Radford was just plain weird, and didn't much care for him. But that didn't bother 'ol Radford a whit 'cause he didn't much care for them neither. Now as it turns out, when it come time to fill out the papers to start that first post office, he come to the line

14

where you fill in the name of the town. Everybody knew the town was called White Oak Flats on account of all the white oak trees around, but Radford up and wrote "Gatlinburg" on that line and by the time anybody found out about it, it was too late. That put folks off a considerable bit, and by 1859 they finally had enough of his shenanigans, and run him out of town.

Today, you will still meet Ogles, Huskys, McCarters, Regans, Ownbys, and Bohannans, but not so many Gatlins. The cabin that Martha Ogle built still stands today, just a short walk from downtown Gatlinburg, a monument to the founding of "The Land of Paradise." And I recon Radford got the last laugh, 'cause White Oak Flats is called Gatlinburg to this very day.

The Richest Lawyer in Sevier County History

The other day I had to go down to the Sevier County Courthouse there in Sevierville, to get a tag renewed. It's a beautiful old courthouse, with a shiny golden dome on top, and is home to the world famous Dolly statue. Everyone knows Dolly Parton. Anyways, it reminded me about this story I heard about the richest lawyer in Sevier County history.

Way back in 1898, just two years after the courthouse was finished, there was the trial of the century there that set up a poor young country lawyer by the name of Eli Burnett, for the rest of his life. John J. Trotter owned one of the most successful business of the time, Trotter Transports. Now this was before the railroad connected Sevierville to Knoxville, and Trotter owned a fleet of flatboats that floated goods up and down the French Broad River back and forth to Knoxville.

Trotter had an accountant named Cook who was a fine accountant, despite the fact he could neither hear nor speak. And after a time it seems Cook got a little greedy and began to siphon off a little cash from the books. Well by the time Trotter found out, some $5000 was gone. Now the only reason he got caught was dumb luck. One of Trotter's bigger accounts was Knoxville Mercantile, and Trotter just happened to run into their Accounts Manager at a Chamber of Commerce meeting and he said in passing that Trotter was the only account he handled that required cash transactions. This was news to Trotter, so he confronts Cook, and looks in the books and can't find Knoxville Mercantile at all.

So he calls the law and they come down and pick up Cook. Now because Cook was a deaf mute, he hired the only lawyer he could communicate with, Eli Burnett. Burnett had learned sign language 'cause he had a deaf sister, and was mighty glad to get the work, 'cause he was just starting out and didn't have any clients to speak of.

So the day of the big trial arrives and folks from all over come to see, on account that there's not much else to do. The courtroom is packed, and Cook is on the stand and the persecuting attorney is questioning him and Burnett is translating.

Now everybody knew Cook was guilty, but he had done a pretty good job of fixing the books, and they searched high and low and couldn't find the money. So Cook is acting all innocent, and denying everything. The prosecutor says,

"You are the accountant for Mr Trotter?"

And Burnett signs to Cook, and Cook shakes his head and signs back to Burnett, and Burnett says,

"He says he was, but Trotter done fired him."

And the people there in the courtroom start snickering a little, so the judge bangs his gavel and everybody quietens down. Then the prosecutor says,

"Well while you were, did you and you alone handle the accounts for Knoxville Mercantile?"

And Burnett translates, and Cook shakes his head and he signs to Burnett and Burnett says,

"He says he recons that Knoxville Mercantile has their own accountant."

There's another bit of laughing and gavel banging, and when that's over the prosecutor says,

"Did you not, on behalf of Mr Trotter, accept cash on the account of Knoxville Mercantile, and divert said cash to your own account?"

Burnett does his thing and Cook shakes his head and does his thing and Burnett says,

"He says he ain't got no account."

Well this time the whole courtroom busts out laughing and even the judge is trying not to laugh while he's hollerin',

"Order! Order in this court!"

Ol' Trotter is sitting there getting pretty mad, 'cause $5000 is a whole lot of money in those days. Finally, he just can't take it anymore, and jumps up, pulls out a pistol and sticks it right in Cook's face! I guess the metal detectors were broken that day. Anyway, he's got that gun right up against Cook's nose and he says,

"Boy, we all know you're as guilty as sin, so you better just tell me where you hid my money or I'm going to blow you to kingdom come!"

Cook is looking down that barrel, and glances over to Burnett, and Burnett furiously signs the message to Cook.

Cook looks at the gun, and looks at Burnett and back at the gun, and signs,

"OK. You got me. I hid the money in a box buried under the sapling back behind my barn."

Trotter looks at Burnett, Burnett looks at Cook, Cook looks at that pistol, and Burnett looks at Trotter, takes a deep breath and says,

"He says you ain't got the guts to pull that trigger."

And that is how Eli Burnett became the richest lawyer in Sevier County history.

In The Glow of The Lightning Bugs

Once each year here in the Smokies, there is a natural phenomena where all the fireflies synch up their glowing. Science has tried to figure out just why this happens, and there are many theories, but this is by far my favorite. You see...

Before they were lightening bugs, they were just... bugs. Each night they would gather around the campfire to listen to the master storyteller spin his tales of truth. There was one little bug who loved the stories so much, that the master gave him the job of gathering stories from all over the world and sharing them with others, so that they may never be forgotten. And to light his way, he gave him the ability to glow like the embers of the fire. The more stories he gathered, the brighter his glow, and as he shared the stories, those he shared with began to glow too. And tales of truth and light covered the entire world as each who heard caught fire. Now once a year, the lightening bugs gather to celebrate the stories, and if you listen closely, you too will begin to glow.

There's a thin golden line, connecting all time
In the glow of the lightning bugs
And the magic you see, is that it binds you to me
In the glow of the lightning bugs

And tonight our hearts beat together
Though it's true we may never pass this way again
The memories we made, forever will remain
In the glow of the lightning bugs

Tonight we have come together to share this wonderful experience of song and tales old and new. And even though everyone of us is different, our sizes and shapes, the color of our eyes and hair, where we come from, and where we are going, tonight we have shared a common experience that will bind us together just as sure and strong as time.

Now, you have become a part of my experience, and I thank you. And I have become a part of your history as well. And as long as the lightning bugs glow on a warm summer night, I will remember you.

'Cause tonight our hearts beat together
Though it's true we may never pass this way again
The memories we made, forever will remain
In the glow of the lightning bugs

Chapter Two

Tall Tales From The Lumbercamp

Lumberjacks?
In the Smokies?

Back in the early 1900's almost every structure in the entire United States was made of... wood. And between 1901 and 1939 a whole lot of that timber came from these Great Smoky Mountains. That was when Colonel Wilson Townsend operated the Little River Lumber Company and the Little River Railroad. He purchased almost 80 thousand acres of land, about one fifth of what is now the Great Smoky Mountain National Park, hired hundreds of workers and began logging operations.

Because of the wild terrain of the Smokies, normal methods of timber removal, such as floating timber to the mill on rivers and streams were not possible. So Colonel Townsend laid over 150 miles of rail to pull the timber out of those rugged mountains. As they moved their logging operations further and further up into the mountains, the railroad made it possible for folks from Knoxville and surrounding areas to explore the Smokies for the very first time. Chairs were placed on flat cars originally made to carry timber, and riders hung on for dear life as they rode through the beautiful mountains. Former logging camps such as Tremont and Elkmont became vacation destinations, and the Wonderland Hotel and the Appalachian Hiking Club were built to accommodate the growing tourist industry.

By the 1920's a movement began to create a National Park to conserve the land, and Colonel Townsend sold all of his timberland that lay within the proposed park boundaries to the movement, insuring federal financial participation.

Since 1934 the National Park has become the most visited national park in the United States and home to one of the most diverse ecosystems in the world.

Some of the following stories and songs were written for the Lumberjack Feud, a dinner show here in Pigeon Forge that celebrates the contributions of Colonel Townsend and all of the hard working men and women in the logging industry that opened the door for exploration of our beautiful Great Smoky Mountains.

The Lumberjacks in the Smokies

Oh! The lumberjacks in the Smokies
are a rough and rowdy pack
They can chop down trees blindfolded
with one hand behind their back
All year long they log these hills
and never stop to rest
But today's the day that they compete
to see just who's the best

So come on all you Dawsons!
Come on you McGraws!
This feud's begun, who's number one
with your axes and your saws?
And give a big "Yo-Ho!"
like the lumberjacks all do
At the axe throwin', log rollin'
Lumberjack Feud

You hear that friends? A big Yo-Ho! That's how we communicate with each other up here in these Smoky Mountains. So anytime somebody gives you a Yo-Ho, it's your duty as proud Dawsons and red blooded McGraws to give 'em one right back! So let's give it a try! Yo-Ho! That's how it's done!

Oh! The lumberjacks in the Smokies,
sure love to jaw and fight
If the Dawsons say a skunk is black,
a McGraw will swear it's white
They've come down from the mountains
to climb and saw and chop
And it's up to you to cheer 'em on
and bring 'em out on top

So come on all you Dawsons!
Come on you McGraws!
This feud's begun, who's number one
with your axes and your saws?
And give a big "Yo-Ho!"
like the lumberjacks all do
At the axe throwin', log rollin'
Lumberjack Feud

Sawdust making, earth shaking
Chips 'a flyin', electrifying
Tree choppin', jaw dropin'
Lumberjack Feud! Yo-Ho!

Bear Scat Pie

*Now you may be a wonderin'
how a cook I came to be
At this rough and tumble timber camp
in the hills of Tennessee*

Well children, the lumber camps don't hire no professional chefs, they provide the stove and pots and pans and such, but the men select the cook from amongst the rank and file. Now they do not select a man that wants to cook, nor one that may be good at it, but rather there's a long standing tradition among the lumberjacks that the one that complains about the food the most is elected to be the chef. In the spring of '29 that someone was me. Now I didn't want the job, and wasn't very good at it neither, but them wily old jacks knew better than complain lest they take my place. So after several weeks of them grinning down runny eggs and salty cakes, I finally saw my chance. There was a new man starting in who had been working timber up near Virginia, and came down to the Smokies to get away from some trouble or another. Well I set out to make this greenhorn our new head chef.

After breakfast the day he was set to arrive, I slipped out behind the canteen to have a smoke and ponder the situation a bit, when I looked down to see the biggest pile of bear scat I had ever seen! I recon ol' Sawyer had been helping hisself to our leftovers, and even a bear couldn't hang on to the swill I'd been feeding those lumbermen for too long. Well as I stood there over that mound an idea crept up slowly like the dawn of a new day, and then all at once the heavens tore open with a flash of lightening and a mighty clap of thunder! And as that roaring rolled into the distance I clearly heard the angels whisper in my ear – Bear Scat Pie.

I ran back into the kitchen and prepared my finest pie crust, carefully pinching the edges into little peak and valleys like I'd seen my Ma do, then went back out to load in my pie filling. I rolled out some dough and cut it into strips and crisscrossed it on top. Then I put it in the oven and cleared out. I don't know if any of you have made scat pie before, but for those of you that have not, well let's just say when the internal temperature reaches a certain point there is an aroma beyond description. After the allotted hour or so, I clamped a clothes pin on my nose and took my pie from the oven and took it a few hundred yards from the canteen to cool.

Now along about seven o'clock I was putting the finishs on what I was certain was to be my last supper for the jacks when the boss came in with the biggest man I ever laid eyes on. He must have been six foot forty, and weighed up near 400 pounds of pure muscle. He had a beard a full foot long, and big black bushy eyebrows that met in the middle over the coldest, blackest little snake eyes that say "I just don't care whether I hits or strikes." His hands were like giant sledge hammer heads, hanging from the ends of tree trunks. Boss says, "This here's the new man Jake." It then occurred to me that I may have made an error concerning my choice of replacement.

But not being a man of towering intellect, I elected to proceed with my plan and after the last biscuit sopped the last bit of gravy from the last plate, I brought from the kitchen... dessert. And in a congenial gesture as to welcome the newest member of our little community, I set that delicacy before Big Jake, and he took a slice and picked it up in that huge paw and took a bite. I was watching his face close as his taste buds decoded the flavor. Then Big Jake jumped to his feet, spit out his bite of pie and roared "This is Bear Scat Pie!"

A frozen stillness fell over the entire camp. Time stood still. The crickets stopped chirping and my blood ran cold. And with every eye in the camp trained upon him, and as a man privy to the ways of the logging camp he continued, "Ain't bad though."

Up At the Camp Canteen

Well I came down from the lumber camp the sun was shining bright
The snow was falling up the hill 'cause it rained all day that night
The chickens swam into the pot, the mess was awful neat
But the lumberjacks weren't hungry so they all stood up to eat

So lay down your axes brothers, lay down your saws
Wash your face and hands and get 'em clean (get 'em clean)
It's time for supper, brothers sit down to eat
Up at the Camp Canteen

Well the Camp Canteen's a happy place where everyone is mad
They laugh and sing the days away 'cause they're so stinkin' sad
Black bears wash the dishes and the meat is cooked by mice
The sugar bowl is filled with salt, and the hot soup's solid ice

So lay down your axes brothers, lay down your saws
Wash your face and hands and get 'em clean (get 'em clean)
It's time for supper, brothers sit down to eat
Up at the Camp Canteen

Someone's in the kitchen with Cookie
Someone's in the kitchen I know
Someone's in the kitchen with Cookie
Strumming on the old banjo

So lay down your axes brothers, lay down your saws
Wash your face and hands and get 'em clean (get 'em clean)
It's time for supper, brothers sit down to eat
Up at the Camp Canteen

32

Dawson And The Strawboss

Ezekiel Jeremiah Dawson was 29 years old when he started logging. His brother Amos brought him into the camp from up in the mountains where he had lived completely alone for better than 12 years. To say he was odd wouldn't approach the matter. He was a dang fine lumberjack, an ax man, hard working but hardly spoke a word to anybody. 'Cept ever now and again, he'd open up, wide open, and go off on some crazy thing or another. For some unknown reason he did not like Babe Ruth. And from time to time he'd wake up the entire bunkhouse in the middle of the night, making some kind of bird noises, and turn up gone for two or three days. He'd always come back though, and never said anything about where he'd been. The Jacks knew he was squirrely, so no one said a thing. I suppose living by his self all those years. Anyways, seems everybody had a story about Zeke Dawson.

One such story was told by Rafe Edwards. He had worked side by side with Zeke most of the time he was in camp. Seems he and Zeke were clearing a little hillside, normal as you please, nary a word between them, when Zeke spies the Straw Boss watching from the top of the hill. All of a sudden, out of the wild blue, Zeke says, "Humph. We do all the work and he just stands there. And I'd bet he's making more money than both you and me put together."

Now Rafe was struck dumb 'cause he ain't never heard Zeke say nothing without being asked, so it takes a second for him to gather up his wits, and when he does, Rafe says, "How do you recon you get a job like that?" And Zeke just grunts, so Rafe goes on. "Why don't you run on up there and ask him?" But Zeke just keeps on clearing, like he never brought it up in the first place, and after a bit, Rafe starts to wonder if the sun had got to him and he'd just imagined the whole thing. But then Zeke stops, stands completely still for a solid minute, then he drops his ax and starts up that hill.

Now according to Rafe, when Zeke got to the boss they have a few words Rafe can't quite make out, and then the boss puts his hand up against a great big pine right there and Rafe hears him say to Zeke, "Hit my hand." So Zeke looks at the Boss, then down to Rafe, shakes his head and rares back and takes a big 'ol swing at the boss' hand! But just before he hits, Boss pulls his hand away, and Zeke smashes his fist right into that tree!

Well sir, he lets out a yell and starts jumping around holding his hand and dog cussin' and all. When he settles down a bit, Boss pats Zeke on the shoulder and Zeke makes his way back down the hill. Rafe's all wide eyed and says, "What'd he say? What'd he say?" And Zeke says,

"He says he got to be boss because he's got brains." Rafe says,

"Brains? What's that mean?" And Zeke holds his hand up in front of his face and says,

"Hit my hand."

The Ballad of Old Man Dawson

Well, Old man Dawson, was a lumberjack,
Shaved his face with a timber ax,
Combed his hair with a chicken wing
Took a bath most every spring

Get out the way! Old Man Dawson,
You're too late to do your chopping
The fire's a burning and supper's cooking
Old Man Dawson just standing there looking

Old man Dawson rode a bear
Down the mountain to the fair
The bear roared and then he jumped
Landed Ol' Dawson on his rump

CHORUS

Old man Dawson climbed a tree
Stirred up a great big hive of bees
Dropped his saw and off he run
Jumped into the saw mill pond

CHORUS

Now old man Dawson loved to dance
In his favorite Sunday pants
Pick the banjo, saw that fiddle
Split his pants right up the middle

CHORUS

Why There Are So Many Pancake Houses in the Smokies

Living here in the Pigeon Forge, tourist are always asking me two questions. One, "Do you see Dolly in the grocery store?" I tell them yes. And number two, "Why are there so many pancake houses in the Smokies?" Well I did a little research on the subject, and this is what I found out.

Way back in Nineteen thirty-three,
in a logging camp up in East Tennessee
A Smoky Mountain tradition there was born,
The camp cook Dixie was a homely girl,
but it was known throughout the logging world
That she made the finest pancakes under the sun

And a logging camp runs on its camp canteen,
so they treated Ol' Dixie just like a queen
They knew her enchanted pancakes was the key their success
So those in charge deemed it essential
that she keep her recipe confidential
'Cause all them other camps will try and bring you down
when they know you're the best

And over at the Wheeler camp, there arose an evil plan
Their camp cook was Flapjack Jones,
the Smokies most handsome man
Although he was a handsome feller, his chow was second rate
And he schemed to steal Dixie's recipes,
so he asked her for a date!

He'd show that gal a little attention,
Oh. Did I happen to mention
That Flapjack was the man of Dixie's dreams?
He'd whisper sweet nothings in her ear,
pull her strings like a puppeteer
And in no time at all, she'd spill the beans

So he called her on the telephone,
and asked her if she might be at home
On Friday night, as he'd like to visit soon
He told her she'd been on his mind,
and he thought that if she had the time
They might take in that harvest moon

Now Dixie was suspicious, but flattered too,
so she agreed to a rendezvous
And Flapjack romanced that homely girl
for the better part of an hour
He whispered "If you really care for me,
you'll share your pancake recipe"
And in a moment of weakness she confessed
"It's magic flour."

"There came a knockin' at my door
one dark and stormy night
And I took in a poor beggar woman
by the name of Martha White
She was soaking wet and hungry,
and she shivered from the cold
So I warmed her by the fireplace
and I fed this poor old soul

And for my kindness she gave to me,
a magic flour tin
And no matter how much I take out
there's always more within.
I believe Miss Martha White
was an genie in disguise
'Cause all my pancake flip themselves,
through the magic of Hot Rize."

Hot Rize. Get it? It's Martha White.
Anyway

Flapjack smiled, that sly old fox
and on his way out he stole that magic flour box
And mixed up a batch of batter,
but much to his chagrin,
The pancakes he made still tasted like glue
or something you'd scrape off the bottom of your shoe
But undeterred, he went back to try again

He turned on his boyish charms,
and once again she melted in his arms
He wooed and cooed Miss Dixie,
with words as smooth as silk
And as he kissed her on the lips,
unknowingly she let it slip
"The secret to my pancakes is...
they're made with magic milk."

"I've got a cow named Bessie,
I raised her from a calf
I put her on a diet
now she gives half and half!
One udder gives butter!
Another udder, cheeses!
And on a cold day Bessie gives sorbet,
and yogurt when she sneezes!"

Yogurt when she sneezes. I don't care who you are, that's funny.
You may think it's organic, but it's snot.

Flapjack give her a kiss and headed on home
and the very next morning Dixie's cow was gone
And the batter he mixed up
seemed a little bit... wetter
With magic dry and magic wet
these pancakes had to be the best ones yet
But when they were done
they weren't no better

And a lesser man might have been done with it,
but Flapjack didn't know the meaning of quit
So that very night he went back down
to plead and beg
But she cut to the chase just quick as the dickens,
flat out told him, "I've got magic chickens,
And all my magic hens
lay magic eggs."

40

"I whipped up a chocolate cake
and it was in the oven baking,
When suddenly, out of the clear blue sky,
the ground began a shaking
And now, every egg my chickens lay
is scrambled in the shell
I recon it was that earthquake,
that shook them all to... pieces."

Sigh.

Pre-scrambled eggs make smoother batter,
fluffier pancakes on the platter
So on his way out
he raided the chicken coop
But by now I recon you know the score,
his pancakes turned out just like before
So one last time he headed on down to Dixie's stoop

With his hat in hand, his pride in check,
his head a' hanging low
He reflected on what he'd started,
just a few days ago
He'd set out to steal Dixie's recipe,
but he kept on getting burned
Seems like every time that he pulled up a chair,
the tables had been turned

Now the best laid plans of mice and men,
often go agley
Sometimes it's the player,
that finds that he's been played
And there in Dixie's parlor
she laid out her final deal
She said, "If you'll agree to marry me,
I'll share my pancake recipe,
All my pancake secrets I'll reveal!"

Well Flapjack never thought,
he could be so easily caught,
He's not the kind of fish that swallows a hook
And Dixie's lack of sex appeal,
wasn't what you'd call ideal,
But boy oh, boy that ugly gal could cook!

And his future at the Wheeler Camp
wasn't looking any brighter
And to tell the truth in these last few days
he'd kind of come to admire her
So he agreed, the pact was made
and they sealed it with a kiss
At least he wouldn't starve to death,
and the story ends like this:

She lead him through the forest
and down a little hill
And there in a clearing
he saw a moonshine still

She poured brown sugar in the mash
and strained it extra fine
Turns out Miss Dixie's secret is...
"The syrup's spiked with shine!"

Moonshine that is. Tennessee tiger sweat. Hillbilly jet fuel.

Now folks from all across this nation,
come to the Smokies for their vacation
Guided by a sweet and sticky vision
They wake their kids and grab their spouse
and take 'em on down to the pancake house
Every morning, for Dixie's Smoky Mountain tradition

It's those magic pancakes you see
that gives them all that energy
To play all day and at night,
to raise the roof
With their eyes a bulging, and bellies growing,
they keep on eating without ever knowing
The syrup they're pouring on is ninety proof!

Our pancakes got quite a kick!
Make you feel real good!
Come get yourself a short stack! Ya hear?

Trading Post

It's Saturday and my chores are done got on my Sunday best
The saws are sharp and the dogs are fed but I ain't got time to rest
Worked real all week long, there's one thing on my mind
I'm headed to the Tradin' Post to see that gal of mine

All week long we chop down trees and float them to the mill
On Saturday we pause to rest and we roll on down the hill
Boss man says I earned my pay so I leave my cares behind
And head down to the Tradin' Post to see that gal of mine

Chorus

I'm headed to the Tradin' Post there's so much there to see
Headed to the Tradin' Post boys don't wait up for me
From the mountain top through Timber Ridge
and the sawmill down the line
I'm headed to the Tradin' Post to see that gal of mine

There comes a time in a loggers life when he lays his ax aside
And if he's good St. Pete will throw those pearly's open wide
Now I don't care if there's streets of gold or mansions silver lined
But I hope they got a Tradin' Post and to see that gal of mine

Chorus

Dolphus Sells Toothbrushes

There's a place that I once heard of,
it's where I'm bound to go
It's a land of milk and honey,
where the streets are paved with gold
The sun is always shining,
where no one wears a frown
There's a fortune for the taking
in Knoxville town

Dolphus Anderson weren't cut out to be a lumberjack. He was smallish and a little frail, but what he lacked in physical stature he more than made up for in cleverness. Not book learning, though. Heck he didn't finish the third grade before his momma died from the typhoid fever and his daddy brought him to the logging camp, where he went to work in the camp canteen washing dishes and cleaning up after the lumberjacks. But he had the kind of cleverness that comes from listening and watching and keeping your mouth shut.

And Dolphus was an ambitious man. He had figured that the best way to make his fortune was through the art of sales. See, he had listened faithfully to the Grand Ol' Opry and Knoxville's Mid-Day Merry Go Round on the radio, and had paid careful attention to the announcers as they pitched the salves and other wares that made the whole thing possible, and he had correctly deduced that the man what did the singing was a working for the man what did the selling. And that feller was making that Merry Go Round.

45

No one there goes hungry,
there's a place that's set for you
Meat and tater's every meal
and pie after you're through
The coffee's always piping hot,
and the biscuits golden brown
There's a fortune for the taking
in Knoxville town

So bright and early one fall morning, with the good will of the entire camp behind him, he set out with nothing more than the clothes on his back, his mother's bible, a ten cent copy of "Think and Grow Rich" that he had wore plum out, some old pots and pans that Cookie had given him, and a dollar and eighty five cents in his pocket. He made his way down the mountain and along the mud rut pathway that is now the Chapman Highway to the big city of Knoxville. He walked across the Gay Street bridge, past the Andrew Johnson Hotel, right into the heart of the city, with all the confidence of the ignorant. He was amazed by the size of the buildings, and startled by the noise of the automobiles and the hustle and bustle of the people. But in his heart he knew this was his town! He turned down a side street just past the Tennessee Theater, down a steep little hill and there, just where it levels out, he came face to face with his destiny, the AJ Arnold Toothbrush Manufacturing, Sales and Service Company.

Poor folks live in mansions,
as tall as they are wide
There's statues on their balconies,
and the outhouse is inside
There's entire rooms for dancing
and the beds are softest down
There's a fortune for the taking
in Knoxville town

He pushed open the plate glass door and strode into the office across what he was to find out was called "carpet" and over to a man sitting behind a big desk and said, "I am the greatest salesman in the world so I might as well be selling your toothbrushes!" The man looked up and peered over his glasses at Dolphus and said,

"You get on out of here boy, we don't want your kind around here!" Dolphus wasn't put off a bit, that man didn't know him at all, much less what kind he was, so he rared up and said,

"I thought you all sold toothbrushes" and the feller said,

"We do, but you don't, now git!" And Dolphus said,

"I'll Suwanee that I can out sell every man you got and then some!" And the man was taken aback for a moment, because he had attended Suwanee College in Georgia and thought Dolphus had mentioned his alma-mater, but by the time he realized his mistake he had already hit upon a plan to get rid of him. He says,

"Lookie here boy, I'm going to give you five toothbrushes. If you can sell them today you come back here and we'll talk about a job."

All the ladies there are dainty,
and pretty as a rose
They'll smile at perfect strangers,
and hardly wear no clothes
With big blue eyes and golden hair
topped with a diamond crown
There's a fortune for the taking
in Knoxville town

47

Well Dolphus grabbed them toothbrushes and hit the door. He was gone about thirty minutes when he came back in and slapped the money down on the mans desk and said, "How about that job?" The man looked up all surprised and says,

"How about that! But that was just a little test." Dolphus says,

"Well bring on the big 'un!" and the man gives him a box of 25.

"You sell these and I'll give you that job!" and Dolphus hits the door! He's gone about an hour and comes back in and slaps that money right on the desk, and the man looks at that pile of money and says, "Well boy, you sure can sell, but the most any man has sold in a day is 100 toothbrushes. If'n you can top that I'll make you the sales manager!" Ol' Dolphus grabs that box and says,

"Mister, you got 'em they need 'em and I'm a gonna get them to 'em!" And he heads out!

> At night folks stroll down lighted streets
> to see a picture show
> Or listen to the Opry
> on their radio
> Concerts, plays and vaudeville,
> the biggest stars around
> There's a fortune for the taking
> in Knoxville town

About two hours go by and the big plate glass door opens and Dolphus comes a gliding across that carpet like a ship across calm waters, and commences to pulling folding money out of his bibs and lays it in front of that man with a smile a mile wide.

Well Ol' Arnold jumps up and whoops! He grabs Dolphus and hugs him and says "Lordy son! I don't know how you did it but I'm hoping you can do it some more! You got the job but you got to tell me how you do it!" Dolphus says,

"I'll do you one better, I'll show you!" And the man grabs his hat and a box of brushes and off they go!

They go around the corner to Cas Walkers grocery store, and Dolphus goes in and comes back with a big bag of potato chips. Then he gets two big bowls, fills one with chips and the other with dip. Then he sets up this sign that he made from the cover of that "Think and Grow Rich" book that says, "Free Chips and Dip!" Before long this rich looking feller comes up, grabs him a chip and fills it slap full of that dip and takes a big ol' bite! Then he starts spitting and sputtering and wiping his mouth and says,

"Boy! That dip taste like dog poop!"

Dolphus says, "It is. You want to buy a toothbrush?"

Summertime is never hot
and winter's never cold
The weather vane is rusted,
'cause the wind don't never blow
And when it rains there's pennies
a' falling to the ground
There's a fortune for the taking
in Knoxville town
I'm bound to claim my fortune
in Knoxville town

49

Chapter Three

Excerpts from the Bestseller "How To Be A Lumberjack"

#18
"How to Dress Like
a Lumberjack"

There has been a style revelation in the last few years with the fashion world embracing the look of the lumberjack. Beards, boots and flannel are showing up on the runway in New York, Paris and Milan. We as lumberjacks approve this movement. Suspenders and Buffalo plaid look good on everyone, especially women. Wool hats are worn equally well by both men and women. But not beards. Beards are for men.

This new fashion statement is called "lumbersexual" but a more accurate description is "Faux jack." Real lumberjacks don't give a rats patootie about what the fashion world does. And we are certainly not concerned that we might be mistaken for a faux jack. You see, it's all in the pants.

The faux jack rolls his pants up to show off his Toby Black boots. A real lumberjack never rolls his pant legs up unless he's log rolling. There's snakes out there. The faux jack pays $120 for his pants, the lumberjack pays $20. The faux jack wears his pants two sizes too small. The lumberjack opts for more room in the crotch area, it's necessary. Suspenders and a belt? Is this a bar or a retirement home?

You want to dress like a real Lumberjack? Dress with purpose. Is it cold outside? Wear flannel. Is it hot? Cut off your sleeves. Tank tops are for women. And Frenchmen. Log rolling? Roll those pants up or better yet, cut them off, they only cost $20. But not too high, the only person that ever looked good in capris was Mary Tyler Moore. Wear steel toed boots, they protect your toes and the extra weight will help make your calf muscles look good when you're log rolling.

So there you go. One more lumberjack skill you can master to be the lumberjack God intended for you to be.

Be a Lumberjack.

Yo Ho! the Timber Tops

Yo ho! the timber top the tippy-top of the mountain oh
Yo ho! the timber top the tippy-top of the mountain oh

And on the top there was a tree,
a rare tree and a rattling tree
There's a tree on the top
At the tippy-top of the mountain oh

Yo ho! the timber top the tippy-top of the mountain oh
Yo ho! the timber top the tippy-top of the mountain oh

On that tree there was a branch
a rare branch and a rattlin' branch...
there's a branch on the tree,
and the tree on the top
At the tippy-top of the mountain oh

On that branch there was a twig
a rare twig and a rattlin' twig...
There's a twig on the branch
and a branch on the tree,
and the tree on the top
At the tippy-top of the mountain oh

On that twig there was a nest
a rare nest and a rattlin' nest...
There's a nest on the twig
and a twig on the branch
and a branch on the tree
and the tree at the top
At the tippy-top of the mountain oh

In that nest there was an egg,
a rare egg and a rattlin' egg...
There's an egg in the nest
and a nest on the twig
and a twig on the branch
and a branch on the tree
and the tree on the top
At the tippy-top of the mountain oh

In that egg there was a bird,
a rare bird and a rattlin' bird...
There's a bird in the egg
and an egg in the nest
and a nest on the twig
and a twig on the branch
and a branch on the tree
and tree on the top
At the tippy-top of the mountain oh

On that bird there was a feather,
a rare feather and a rattlin' feather...
The feather on the bird
and the bird in the egg
and the egg in the nest
and the nest on the twig
and the twig on the branch
and the branch on the tree
and the tree on the top
At the tippy-top of the mountain oh

Yo ho! the timber top the tippy-top of the mountain oh
Yo ho! the timber top
The tippy-top of the mountain oh!

#20
"How to Grow a Lumberjack Beard"

All week long you sit at your desk in front of your computer and hardly see the light of day. You've gotten flabby and weak, and at the end of the day, you don't have enough energy left to go out with your wife or play with your kids. Things may look bleak, but friend, there is hope. Deep inside of you there's a lumberjack just waiting to get out.

Hello kids, Uncle Bud Beasley here with another tip to help you let out your inner lumberjack. The North American Lumberjack can be immediately recognized by his lumberjack beard. A goatee is not a lumberjack beard. Neither is soul patch. A lumberjack beard is wild. Free. No fancy conditioners or perfumes. A lumberjack beard smells like wood smoke and coffee.

To show the world your inner lumberjack, if you don't have an ax or chainsaw handy, you need a beard. First, get permission from your wife or girlfriend. Just kidding. You're a lumberjack. You don't need permission from anybody.

Your first step is to make up your mind that whatever grows out of your face is OK. God put it there, so it must be alright. Lumberjacks are not overly self-conscious about their looks, and a lumberjack has an inner light that is attractive regardless of how gray or scraggly your beard is.

Step two. Take your drug store razors and throw them away. Especially disposable razors. They are for shaving your legs. Lumberjacks don't shave their legs. That's for women. And Frenchmen. But shaving your neck and non-bearded areas of your face will help your beard stand out. Buy one of these bladed razors or if you're really serious, get one of these straight razors. Not only will it shave closer, but you can work on your honing skills with an old leather belt. And you'll be buying a smaller leather belt because your waist line is getting smaller. You're a lumberjack.

Now it is perfectly acceptable to trim your beard, and to be neat with it. Good grooming has it's place, just don't over do it and never, ever color your beard. Salt and pepper are spices, and if you can achieve silver or gray, you're pretty awesome.

And a final tip, if you have something in your beard and someone points it out to you, the proper response is: "I put it there."

So there you go. One more lumberjack skill you can master to be the lumberjack God intended for you to be.

Be a Lumberjack.

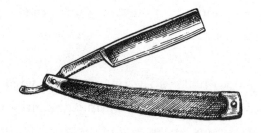

#22
"How to Talk Like a Lumberjack"

Lumberjacks come from all areas of North America. There are lumberjacks in Canada, Tennessee, Oregon, Wisconsin, New York and everywhere in between. And each area has it's own distinct terms, but today we're going to focus on the words and phrases that are common to all lumberjacks.

Say you find yourself in a bar in oh, let's say Ketchican Alaska. And you see a group of lumberjacks coming in from a hard day working in the woods. You know immediately that they are lumberjacks by their confidence and flannel. You also notice that all the women are drawn to their masculine aura. Don't be a poser. Lumberjacks can smell fear a mile away. If you practice these simple rules, you can have confidence that you'll be drawn into their community and maybe attract a girl. Just be aware it will probably be the good looking girls best friend. The one with a "good personality." Don't be greedy. You're a buckwheater. There is term number one. Buckwheater. That's a beginner. Sometimes called a "brush monkey." Don't be upset if someone calls you a buckwheater, it means that you have potential. Those without potential are "wanna be's" or "frenchmen." On the other end of the experience line is the "Timber Beast" or "Savage." Just be careful using this term. Unless you are one, best stick with "Logger." The man in charge is the "Straw Boss." Your "rig" is your equipment. See video #19 "Tools of the Lumberjack" for an overview of a standard "rig." The correct term for cutting down a tree is "felling." "Felling" a section of timber is "harvesting." And try to use the word "timber" as much as possible. Just don't yell it out when you're felling a tree. You'll look like a brush monkey. You may be asked where you are from. Don't say "Los Angles." Say something like "I've been felling timber down in the Clinchs with an outfit out of Saskatchewan."

You may be cornered into telling a story. Just in case this happens, memorize this short tale word for word, whether you understand what you're saying or not.

"We were working the line on a slope and there was a big school marm and no way the steam donkey could get to her. We'd been highballing since the whistle punk come on the talkie tooter, but she was surrounded by a bunch of pecker poles, so we buried a dead man with a haywire extension to the choker, and this buckwheater we were trying to log up set a beaver tail in the bole and made a dutchman, and it barber chaired, and went sky west and crooked, and I thought we are all headed for section 37, and a widow maker flew and hit me and I've been counting the ties and boarding with Aunt Polly for about 3 months." Then just shut up.

And finally, "Yo Ho." Not to be confused with the pirate "Yo Ho Ho," the lumberjack "Yo Ho" can mean several things, like the Hawaiian "Aloha." It can be a greeting, sometimes yelled, "Yo Ho!" Or used as a question mark, "Yo Ho?" Or an ending to a statement. "Yo Ho."

So there you go. One more lumberjack skill you can master to be the lumberjack God intended for you to be.

Be a Lumberjack.

Chapter Four

Real True Personal Stories That You Should Believe

Joe Sharp Fishing Story

So there was this time that me and Crazy Joe Sharp were fishing down by Douglas Dam and... damn.

Now everybody around here knows about Big Ben. Big Ben is a wily old large mouth bass, 10 or 12 pounds. We're talking huge. He hangs out in this little slew right around this stump that sticks out of the water about that high, six or eight feet from the bank. Lots of folks have claimed to have seen him, and a few say they have hooked him, but ain't nobody never caught him, so he's like a legend, right?

Me and Joe are sitting in the boat, doing alright fishing for crappie, and Joe says, "L,l..l...let's go try for Big Ben." He talks like that, you know.

Well we putt putt on over to the slew, and we've thrown the whole tackle box at him. Worms, minnows, jigs, flies, you name it, nothing. Nary a nibble.

We're just about to give up and about that time I look up and this squirrel comes out of the bushes there on the bank and I see he's looking at something. He's like looking... And I look to see what he's looking at and he's looking at that stump there in the water, and I see that there is a big acorn on top of that stump. And he must have wanted it bad, 'cause he backs up a little and takes a flying leap over the water and lands on that stump!

Joe's eyes get real big and he says, "Y, y..y...you see that?"

And I said I did and we laugh a minute and the squirrel is gnawing away on that acorn, and we're watching him, and just then, there's this commotion in the water and all of a sudden, Big Ben comes leaping up out of the water, and swallows that squirrel whole!

Well Joe about jumps out of his skin, and I drop my pole and we nearly tumpt over, and Joe says, plain as day, "Holy sh...cow." Or something like that, and we're trying to process what we have just seen, and my heart starts to slow back down a little and Joe says, "A...a...ain't nobody gonna believe this!"

So just about the time we get settled down a little, there's this big commotion in the water and we turn and look and Big Ben comes jumping up out of the water again, and if I'm lying, I'm dying.

That fish set another acorn on top of that stump. You can believe me if you want to.

Homecoming

It was Mother's Day, 1969. I was eight years old and was at Homecoming, hiding in the graveyard. There is a tradition in rural southern communities for families to get together on special days like Mother's Day and eat and visit and such. My family held our celebration at Oak Grove, a little unincorporated community in North Alabama, picnicking right between the Baptist Church and Methodist Church, under a little grove of oak trees that divided my Baptist Mother's people from my Methodist Father's. My mother was one of seven girls, and my dad had a brother and two sisters, and all told there would be upwards of two dozen cousins there. We called it Homecoming.

These two little churches sat side by side surrounded by hundreds of acres of open farm land and it was the only place I had ever been where you still had to use an out house. There would be dinner on the ground, which some folks call a pot luck, where all my aunts and extended family women folk would compete to take the most disgusting vegetable they could find and make it into a casserole, completely disguising it in cheese. First empty casserole dish wins.

There would be all day preaching, because including my Dad, both Grandfathers, uncles and cousins there were nine preachers vying for pulpit time, and my cousin Faye would get saved. Again. Since I had relatives in both pulpits, I could tell my Mother I was at the Methodist church, and tell my Dad I was at the Baptist, and me and my cousins would play hide and go seek amongst the tombstones in the cemetery.

If kids playing in a cemetery seems odd to you, you are not alone. But I was growing up in a United Methodist Church parsonage sitting right in between the church and the cemetery, and as far as spooks and ghosts are concerned, well I never give it much thought. Now on this particular year, it had just got good dark, and the moon was bright and sitting low in the sky, casting long shadows across the final resting places of my ancestors. Perfect for hiding.

So there I was, hiding behind the grave stone of Duford Hightower, who was a great uncle or something on my mother's side, determined to not get caught first and be "it," when I heard this blood curdling scream coming from somewhere on the other side of the cemetery. Then I saw a few of the kids running, so I got up and we all converged there in the middle of the cemetery around my cousin Renee who was evidently having an "episode." She was shaking and crying and pointing and trying to scream, but nothing was coming out. Her sister Tammy was trying to help her get a hold of herself, and when she finally caught her breath, she choked out one word. "Ghost!"

I would like to point out at this time that Renee was actually my second cousin. Her mother Faye, the one I mentioned earlier, was my first cousin, but she was older and strange. My Momma always looked down and said "bless her heart" a lot whenever she talked about Faye,

66

and Daddy said the whole lot of them were "weirdos" and "excitable" and "prone to exaggeration." But there was no denying Renee had seen something.

As she told it, she was crouched down behind our great, great aunt Helen's marker, when she noticed some movement and turned and looked and there in the moonlight, she saw a white figure floating in the air. It was moving up and down just a couple of feet off the ground, and she was trying to convince herself that she was just seeing things and then it rattled it's chains at her, and let out this low moan, "Ooooooo!"

We are all looking around at each trying not to laugh, and after some discussion, it was decided that the braver among us would investigate. I was pretty sure it would turn out to be nothing at all, but as we walked in the direction she was pointing, I started to feel the hairs on the back of my neck stand up. I wasn't exactly scared, but the closer we got to the edge of the graveyard, the slower we walked. Single file, like on Scooby Doo. We eased past my Mother's twin cousin's Lovie and Dovie's graves, past Great Grandpa and Grandmaw Clark and Uncle Otto, who died in the Korean war, and finally we were at Helen's grave.

Some clouds had moved in front of the moon, so it was pretty dark, and when we looked around, we didn't see anything at all. But then I heard this low moaning sound, and the clouds drifted away and the moon shown bright again, and I turned and looked, and my blood ran cold! Because there, not more than 30 feet away, was a white figure dancing in the moonlight. It rose up from the ground and clanked a bit, moaned again and dipped back down to the ground.

By the time I looked back around, everyone was gone. But in that instant it began to dawn on me just where I had heard that clanging noise before, and just as I got two and two put together, I saw the headlights of a pick up truck coming across the field. And then the lights turned my way and lit up our "ghost." There, scratching her neck on a fencepost was a Black Hereford cow with the whitest face you ever saw! And as she scratched, she expressed her satisfaction with a long and low moo, and that cowbell clanked like the long and ponderous chain that Jacob Marley forged in life and carried with him as he wandered through all eternity.

She had missed her dinner bell. But just like in the bible story, the shepherd left the ninety-nine and found the one. So I recon Bessie had her a homecoming too.

The Christmas Tree Caper

Way back before there were plastic Christmas trees there were aluminum Christmas trees and my mother had the shiniest silver tree you have ever seen, complete with a color wheel that would change the tree from blue to green to red to gold and back to blue. But one Christmas, my Father decided that we should have a real tree.

Now my mother was firmly against this idea, but he had grown up in the country, where there they didn't have artificial trees, so on the Saturday after Thanksgiving he and I set out into the woods with a little pruning saw to find the perfect tree.

It was particularly cold and overcast that day and there was the slightest chance of snow, but we were bundled up pretty good and the excitement of the adventure kept us warm. After walking a little bit, I found this tree I liked, and he came over and looked it up and down, and said, "I think this one is too short, let's keep looking." So we went on for another half hour or so, and I saw this other tree that I thought might do, but he said it wasn't full enough so on we went. Well every tree I picked had this or that wrong with it, and I was getting pretty tired, and it was starting to get dark. But finally, we came into this little clearing where there was a little stream and this beautiful spruce tree, about 12 feet tall and full as can be.

And I must admit, it was worth the wait. So he got down on his hands and knees and crawled up under it with that pruning saw and started sawing away, and the branches were so thick I could only see his feet sticking out from underneath. Well he started sawing and the tree was shaking as he pulled the blade through the trunk, back and forth, back and forth. After a minute or two the sawing started slowing down and my Father started grunting and groaning until finally the sawing stopped completely.

Now I don't know if any of you have ever tried to saw down a tree, but what can happen is that as you saw further into the tree, it will lean a little bit and pinch down on the blade and the weight of the tree slows things down considerable. Well my dads saw was stuck tight in the middle of that tree trunk, but being a stubborn sort and a college graduate, he set down to figure out how to get the blade free and finish the job.

After surveying the situation, he concluded that if we could push the tree in the opposite direction of the pinching, it would free up the blade, so he had me crawl in the branches with him and push on the trunk while he worked the blade free, but at that time I didn't weigh enough to make any difference, so we crawled back out and he thought some more, and pretty soon he figured that this was a geometry problem, and if I climbed up to the top of the tree, my weight times the hypotenuse squared by pi would be enough to unpinch the saw blade.

70

So I climbed up and he crawls under, and he is able to move the blade a quarter inch or so, and he hollers up to me, "Lean out a little!" So I lean back and he hollers, "That's it! Lean some more!" So I lean some more, and he's sawing away and all of a sudden I hear this snap and I'm falling toward the ground on the underside of this tree.

Fortunately, this seems to be happening in slow motion, so by the time I hit the ground I had managed to fling myself away from the tree and didn't get hurt at all. On the other hand, my father who was under the tree did not fair as well. There is a term used in the logging industry called "barber chair." That is when a tree is sawed down the business end will pop up and push back away from the direction it is falling. Every instinct that my father had when that tree started to fall was to move away, but as me and the tree came down, the trunk came up and clipped him under the chin like mother nature gave him an uppercut.

To further complicate the situation, the tree falling stirred up a nest of wasps who promptly attacked both he and I, but he got the worst of it because I ran away and he was still a bit dazed from the uppercut. I stood a safe distance away and watched amazed as he swatted those wasps away, but they were persistent, and he staggered around until suddenly he got too close to that stream, tripped on a rock and fell backwards into the water.

Well, after all the dust and wasps had settled, he crawled out and we went back in to claim the tree. He was stung up pretty good, and by the time we got it back to the car it was pitch dark, and of course, the tree was to big to bring in the house, so he had to cut about four feet off the bottom, and we still had to move the furniture around to make room for it and the next year and every year after, we had a traditional 1960's

71

aluminum Christmas tree, with the color wheel that changed the tree from blue, to green, to red, to gold and back to blue again.

But on the bright side, it was the only time I ever saw someone use geometry in real life.

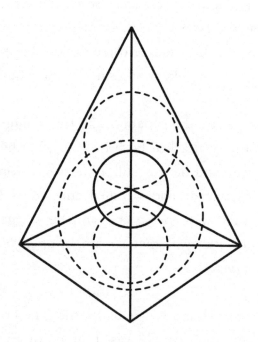

Grand Pa's New Car

My Grandpa Clark had the first Ford Model T automobile in Franklin County Alabama. His brother Otto, took him in the wagon to Russellville where he got on the bus and rode to Nashville, then he walked six blocks down to the Ford dealership and paid cash money for a shiny black Model T. They took that money and handed him the keys, and off he went. The only problem was, Grandpa did not know how to drive.

Now this was back before a driver's license was a deal, matter of fact, roads weren't much of a deal either. Nor road signs or maps, but folks back then just sort of knew which direction was South and Grandpa went that way.

He kinda knew about steering from driving horse drawn wagons and such, and figured out the clutch and gear box as he went along, from that summer he worked at the mill. He went pretty slowly I recon. 'Cause it took him 13 hours to travel the 170 miles back home, averaging a little better than 13 miles per hour. The entire trip had lasted almost 19 hours, in which time he had not slept, but the stress of not knowing what he was doing kept him going.

Along about 9am the next morning, my Mother and her sisters were interrupted from their chores by an unfamiliar sound. And when they looked out, they saw Grandpa chugging up the road with the top down and his driving gloves and goggles on. He was followed by most of the inhabitants of Franklin County, who had heard him coming, and started in behind him in a make shift parade. Folks in wagons and on horseback, and some just walking alongside Grandpa, chatting him up and asking questions and such.

And he had mostly figured the thing out, except for one thing. You see, he was going so slow he hadn't needed to use the brakes, and frankly, he didn't know he had them. But as he pulled up to the house he saw the need for something to stop him, and he drove around and around the house, pulling on the steering wheel and hollering "Whoa!" while Grandma and the kids chased him around squealing and laughing.

Finally he figured the only way to stop was to hit something, so he headed for the field and drove into a big pile of hay and stopped. He crawled out, took off his gloves and goggles, and left the automobile right where it stopped underneath that haystack. Later that morning he wrote a letter. We are not sure of exactly what he wrote, but we can make some assumptions based on this letter that he received the following week. It reads, "Dear Mr. Clark, Congratulations on the purchase of your new Model T Ford automobile. We here at the Ford Motor Company are certain it will benefit you, your family and your community for years to come. We appreciate your suggestion regarding stopping the vehicle, and would humbly draw your attention to the three pedals in the floorboard of the automobile. The one on the right is to make it go. The one on the left is for engaging the gears, and the one in the middle is to slow and eventually stop the vehicle. We hope this information extends the life and enjoyment of your new Model T. Sincerely, Henry Ford, President, Ford Motor Company.

The following week they dug the car out and he drove it for the next 40 plus years.

74

Jim Hears From God

Storytellers do not always stick strictly to the truth. Poetic license, it is called. Some just color the details with "as I recall" or "as it was told", and some just flat out lie. But the story that I'm telling you now is the honest to God truth told to you first hand, because I was there, and there are probably a half dozen other eye witnesses that are still living that can back me up.

Two things you need to know. Number one, the acceptable length of a sermon in the United Methodist Church is 20 minutes. You tell 'em what you're going to tell 'em, you tell 'em, and then you tell 'em what you told 'em. Any longer and the Baptist beat you to Cracker Barrel.

Number two, in the summer of 1979 in the hot and humid little river town of Gadsden, Alabama, the CB radio craze was still in full swing, and everyone had their CB handles. "Breaker, breaker 1-9 this here's Ol' Rattler, there's a Full Grown Bear in the bushes with a Bird Dog just past the Chicken Coop on the I-95 Boulevard, a Kojack with a Kodak in a Gumball Machine so ease it on back to double nickles or you'll get your driving award, come back." And they'd say 10-4 and then everybody listening would sing "Convoy."

Now. Jim Nixon was an elementary school principal that felt called to preach later in his life. He was a well educated man, but his strengths lay in school administration, rather than classroom teaching. Fact is, he had shied away from any sort of public speaking, which made his call to the pulpit somewhat uncomfortable, but he figured that his call was real. He had heard the voice of God command him and he believed that God would not lead him where he was not to go, and so he began his tutelage as an associate pastor under the guiding hand of the Rev. J.E. Beasley, my father.

Brother Jim performed all of his church duties with gusto. He worked with the youth, he visited the sick and shut ins, he counseled with folks about to get married, and held the hands of those whose loved ones were laid to rest. He was well liked by the congregation, and became a trusted friend and confidant to my Dad. But the one thing he could not seem to do was deliver a sermon. Most folks called into ministry start with a sermon. They get the call and start right in telling folks all about it. Ready or not, here they come. But maybe because of his education, or maybe his being a little older than most, Brother Jim had a profound respect for the pulpit, and try as he may he never felt quite ready to preach to those who loved him so much. Of course my Dad worked with him every week on helping him develop a good sermon, and would have him practice in front of the big mirror in the choir room, and assure him that everything would be alright, but Jim just couldn't bring himself to pull the trigger.

Finally, after several months of preparation, my Dad insisted that he was ready. And reluctantly, Jim agreed to preach at a upcoming Sunday evening service. Word spread quickly, and on the appointed night, the church house was completely filled with folks there to support Brother Jim. It was a warm summer evening, and everyone seemed to be in great spirits, except for Jim who was sweating like a... well, let's say sinner in church, and looked like he might just pass out. Daddy was all in. He guided the service from the call to worship through the singing and the praying, warming up the crowd for the main event. And he had great

76

faith in Jim and all the work the two had put into that sermon, a fine three pointer based on the story of the leaper healed by his faith. And when he introduced Brother Jim, the congregation beamed up at him and the good vibes rose up to that pulpit so thick you could taste it. Jim held both sides of the podium in a death grip, took a deep breath and began.

What came out was the shortest United Methodist sermon ever recorded. He hit all three points in three minutes flat, and wrapped the whole thing up with the classic, "And now, with every head bowed and every eye closed, let us go to our Father in prayer." And Brother Jim leaned into that prayer. And as he prayed, some of the blood began to return to his head and he became aware of what had just transpired. So in an effort to stretch things out a bit, he began to improvise the prayer. In the pews, we obediently sat with our head bowed, still stunned by the brevity of the message. Well after a minute or so, we became aware of the stark contrast between the length of the sermon the length of the prayer. Jim prayed for the sick and suffering. He prayed for the lost and the weary. He prayed for our service men and women, and those who served our communities at home, our fire and police forces. He prayed for our President, Vice President and all the member of the cabinet and congress, our judges and others associated with the Supreme Court.

Long about here folks started glancing around the room, just wondering where we might be headed. Vietnam. We went to Vietnam and prayed for their people, and then on to China and Africa, and the missionaries who worked to bring the word of God to the third world. Then we made a turn over in Indonesia, and headed straight back home. And then it got personal. Each and every person in that sanctuary was prayed for by name, some with a little detail about the problems they were facing, others with the details gratefully omitted.

And sweat fell like great drops of blood from Brother Jim's forehead and the congregation swung from shocked to amused to uneasy to terrified and back to amused, and exactly 16 minutes after it all started, Brother Jim brought the whole thing to a close with, "All these things we ask in the name of Your Son Jesus Christ, Amen."

What happened next some folks try to explain away by saying that the sound system in that little church was not what you'd call "professional." And it is true that a poorly grounded sound system can receive rogue audio signals from nearby radio stations, or oh, perhaps a CB radio in a pick up truck passing by. But those of us that have more faith that the Almighty God can and will speak directly to a person know exactly what happened.

For as Brother Jim completed his humble, yet epic first sermon, at the exact moment of the "Amen", we all clearly heard the voice of God come through that little church sound system. And God said,

"That's a big 10-4 good buddy."

And all the people said, "Amen." Amen.

The Pell City Tornado

This was back in around 1973 or so. I was only 11 or 12, so the exact year and some details may not be completely accurate. But it was in the spring, which brings forth new life, and in the south, tornadoes. And one such tornado had sat down in Pell City Alabama, which was a few miles away from where we lived in Trussville. I don't remember if there were any injuries, but I do know it made quite a mess with trees down and stuff blown all over.

The United Methodist Men's group at our church had organized a task force to go up and help out where they could. My father, who was the preacher of the church, had decided that it would be a good idea for me to tag along and practice a little local mission work. My Mother was against it, but he said it would do the boy some good to get out and do something for others for a change. She said she thought I was too little, but he said "For Christ sake, Winnie, the boy's nearly a teenager." And finally she said it was okay, just make sure he doesn't get hurt.

Well the big day came and my Mother packed our lunch into my old "Voyage to the Bottom of the Sea" lunch box, gave me a peck on the cheek and a look, like she was losing her baby boy, and off we went, about 20 men with chain saws and rakes and garbage cans all loaded up in the church bus and headed to Pell City. I was pretty excited. I had never seen where a tornado had touched down but I had seen the Wizard of Oz. When we got there, we met up with a bunch of men from the Pell City United Methodist Church, and they took us down to this neighborhood where the tornado had ripped through. I had worked up this scenario in my head where I would be digging through the rubble and find someone, perhaps a pretty girl, still alive buried under there and I'd save her life and be a hero and get a medal or something. But where we were, all of the houses were still standing, so I'd have to be a hero some other day.

This street we were on was right across from a park and on the far side of the park was a little river and there were swings and slides and such for the kids to play on and a big pavilion with picnic tables and a big fireplace at one end. And there were about a hundred or so folks out there cutting up fallen trees and dragging branches up to the road where they had made this long pile for the city to come along and haul it all off. I was assigned to branch dragging duty. It wasn't glamorous, but I was doing my part. And it was kind of fun. Everyone was in good spirits and the men were joking around and we were getting a lot done. But it was hard work, and by lunch time, I was tired and hungry.

We had planned to eat there in the park under that pavilion, so I ran back to the church bus and grabbed my lunch box and ran back over to the picnic tables. I sat down and plopped that lunch box on the table and opened it up. I took out two sandwiches, one for me and one for my Daddy, and then two apples and finally, two packages of Little Debbie Swiss Cake Rolls. I don't know what your childhood was like, but for me, a Little Debbie snack cake was a rare treat, and an event to be savored. Now I had been taught to eat your meal first and save your desert for last. But even at 12 years old I knew life was unpredictable, you might be here one minute and gone the next, and there wasn't an adult around to stop me, so I carefully tore open that cellophane package and stuck my nose right down in there and took a big ol' sniff. Then I pulled out the first of the two Swiss Cake Rolls, and wondered if the children in Switzerland ate these things all the time. I studied the end, where you could see the thin chocolate cake rolled around a layer of cream filling, and blanketed in milk chocolate. There was a little card in the package that the Swiss cakes sat on, and the chocolate had melted against that card and re-hardened, so there was a little flat piece of pure milk chocolate there on the bottom and I broke it off and took a nibble. My eyes rolled back in my head and I drifted off into pure bliss. Had I known the word "Nirvana" I would have used it.

And as I drifted further off into my rapturous state, I was suddenly jerked back to reality by the booming voice of my Father calling my name. He was standing at the other end of that pavilion, and the concrete floor and high wooden ceiling amplified his voice and added some reverb for extra drama. Even though he was born with a big voice, the effect was doubled when he had learned "projection" in preaching school. I whipped around and hid that Little Debbie in my lap, sure that I was caught, but he said that the group had decided to eat under some trees over by the river, and I needed to hurry up and come on. So I put the sandwiches back in the lunch box, and I put the apples back in the lunch box, and then I put the Little Debbie Swiss Cake Rolls back in the lunch box and closed the lid. Then I jumped up, and started running toward my Dad. I was about halfway there when it happened. It must have been a crack in the cement, or perhaps some little debris blown up by the storm, but I tripped on something, and I fell.

Scientist have proven that time is relative. And we all know that five minutes in the dentist chair is infinitely longer than five minutes just about anywhere else, so as I fell, everything went into slow motion.

81

I saw the lunch box extended out in front of me that I was still holding by the handle in my right hand. I saw the clasp that held the lid shut move, just a bit, and then pop loose. I saw the top of that lunch box start to open, and I saw the sandwiches, and the fruit, led by Little Debbie herself forcing their way out of that lunch box to freedom. I saw my left hand move to try and slam it shut before the escape was complete, but it was too late. I watched in horror as my lunch, and my Father's lunch went flying through the air, and I saw my Dad as he saw his lunch fly over his head.

What I did not see was the concrete as it came up to meet me. I was still looking up as my left cheek skidded across that rough concrete floor, and then I saw stars, and then I saw my Dads tennis shoe. I turned my face up to meet the gaze of my father, bruised and bleeding, just as the sinner looks up to his heavenly father for comfort and solace. And just before I passed out I clearly heard my Father's loving voice ring out across that pavilion, "What did you do that for?"

I was okay though. I returned home that night a battle scarred tornado veteran, with a very important life lesson learned.

Although haste may make waste,
A little dirt don't hurt
The taste of a Little Debbie Snack Cake.

Buffalo Gals

I was walking down the street, down the street, down the street,
Pretty little Girl I chanced to meet, Oh! She was fair to view...

When I was a junior at Hewitt Trussville high school back in the 1970's, disco was big all across the country, but not so much in small town Alabama. We liked football and Leonard Skinnard. Our big rivals in football were the Springville Buffalo's, the next small town over, and they were every bit as passionate about their football as we were. They were the enemy, a dark and evil people who inbred football players into slack jawed mutant behemoths, all brawn and no brain. Any self respecting Trussvillian wouldn't be caught dead associating with such. Until I met Amy. I was with some friends at the Eastwood Mall over in the big city when I saw the prettiest girl ever. Blonde hair, blue eyes, and a figure that made the girls I knew look like 10 year old's. She was with a group of her friends and we started talking and then it came up that they were all Springville Buffalo cheerleaders. Well being the son of a preacher, I was raised to not discriminate against anyone, let alone a cute blonde cheerleader. But when I told her I went to Hewitt, those big blue eyes flew wide open and just when I thought I'd seen everything, she gasped, "Do you know Micky Dossey?"

Buffalo gals can you come out tonight, come out tonight, come out tonight?
Oh Buffalo gals can you come out tonight and dance by the light of the moon?

Now this was a strange question because I did know Mickey. I just wasn't sure anyone else did. Much less a cute blonde Buffalo. Mickey was a grade back of me and the only reason I knew him was from the AV club. Tall and skinny, with braces, acne and a head of hair that James Brown would be proud of. He was real quiet most of the time and kind of painfully awkward when he did say something. I was just getting ready to ask her how she knew Mickey, when she threw her arms around my neck and cried, "Could you introduce me to him?" I was a little surprised, so I chuckled a little and said I supposed I could, and just when I thought I'd seen everything, she kissed me! Right on the mouth. I said, "What's your name?" and she said,

"Amy." Amy.

I stopped her and we had a talk, had a talk, had a talk
Her feet took up the whole sidewalk, and left no room for me...

We exchanged telephone numbers, and the very next day after school she calls me. She asked if I might be available to take her out Saturday night. Just when I thought I'd seen everything. At that time in my life I had never had a girl call me, much less ask me for a date. I thought to myself, "Man she really must be crazy about me!" I guess I'd be lying if I suggested that at this time, I was the least bit suspicious. That kiss had totally erased anything she might have said regarding a nerdy sophomore. I asked her where she wanted to go and she said "The Odyssey" which was the teen disco on Morris Avenue in Birmingham. So Saturday rolls around and I get all spiffy'd up, and drive my Hornet hatchback with the Levis seat covers over to Springville. She was even prettier than I remembered. She was waiting on the porch when I drove up and she came running out to my car with those blonde curls bouncing, hopped in, and just when I thought I'd seen everything, she gave me a peck on the cheek and said, "Let's go!"

84

I asked her if she'd have a dance, have a dance, have a dance
I thought that I might have a chance to shake a foot with her

She talked a blue streak all the way to Birmingham, and we listened to WSGN playing all the latest disco hits, and just about dark we turned down Morris Avenue and found a place to park about a block from the Odyssey. There were crowds of kids standing outside in packs, with the boys all eying the girls and the girls pretending not to notice. But I was walking in holding hands with the prettiest girl there. Her excitement seemed to ramp up a bit as we came inside the room filled to the rafters with mostly, girls. And just when I thought I'd seen it all, there on the acrylic dance floor, in the center of a ring of girls staring and oohing and aahing, was Mickey.

I danced with a gal with a hole in her stocking
and her heel kept a rockin' and her toe kept a knockin'
I danced with a gal with a hole in her stocking
and we danced by the light of the moon.

And he was dancing. He had moves that made John Travolta look like, well, Horshack. Every fiber of his being poured into every step, every move. And it wasn't just the standard "Hustle" or "Electric Slide." No, he had added moves within the steps that took it to a completely different level. Fluid, mesmerizing, creative. His dance partners changed every few seconds, and those whose turn it was came in with great excitement and only a few seconds later, wilted back into the crowd exhausted by Mickey's magnetism. I turned to say something to Amy, and she was gone. Then I saw her working her way toward the inner part of the circle. I looked around and saw some guys I recognized from football and walked over to them. We just looked at one another and kind of nodded. There was nothing to say.

A little while later Amy pulled me aside and kissed me on the cheek and told me she had found another ride home and she hoped I understood. And being the worldly man I was, I did.

A few days later I saw Mickey at the AV club meeting and when I caught his eye he just shrugged his shoulders a little bit as if to say, "I don't really understand it myself." So that was that.

I never saw Amy again. Mickey went on to a successful career in computers or something, and me? Well I turned out to be a poet. And the lesson I'm trying to teach you with this story is this: You can't judge a book by it's cover, or a dancer by his acne.

Buffalo gals can you come out tonight, come out tonight, come out tonight?
Oh Buffalo gals can you come out tonight and dance by the light of the moon?

Being Garth

Back in the early 1990's I was a hired gun guitar player in a band that was connected to a company that was a big player in an unspecified industry. The President of this company was a pretty fair musician and had formed this band with other pretty fair musicians within his company. But there were holes in the sound, and there was five of us that were hired to fill those holes. We stood in the back and called ourselves the "Band Trash."

This was a great gig. We played all kinds of really big parties and conventions within this unspecified industry representing this company, where the bars were open and the crowds were large and rowdy. And we actually got paid. We traveled all over the country with all of the amenities of rock stars, except without the women and the drugs. You can't have everything.

Because of our relationship with this company, we also played a lot of fund raisers for various charities, and that is how I found myself in Hollywood California preparing to play on a telethon that would be broadcast all across the United States. Now I don't know how many of y'all have ever participated in a program such as this, but because of copyright laws and such, all the songs must be original or copyright free, and being a party band, we only played cover songs like "Louie Louie" and "Brown Eyed Girl." So it fell to the band trash like myself to submit original material to the President to possibly be used in this performance. And that is how I found myself promoted from back up singing, guitar playing band trash to front man, lip syncing to a recording that we had made of a song that I wrote, called "Work With Your Fingers and Not Your Hands."

For those of you too young to remember, back in the early 90's the country music artists dressed better than the audience. It was hip at the time to wear fancy rhinestone jackets like the ones created by Nudie Cohn for Porter and Hank, and everybody wore cowboy hats whether you were balding or not. Now since I had been moved up front to represent this unspecified company, the President took a look at me and decided I needed a complete make over, and spared no expense in decking me out in the shiniest outfit since Glen Campbell had recorded "Rhinestone Cowboy."

The bolero jacket was purple, and covered in swirls of glitz fashioned from metal studs and faux crystals cascading down the wide lapels, and from the padded shoulders down each arm. My black boot cut jeans came from an exclusive boutique on Rodeo Drive, with each of the hip pockets featuring the same swirl from the jacket, and silver metallic embroidery ran down the sides from the waist to the floor. The concho belt was held together with a buckle that implied that I had won a rodeo championship, and was purely decorative, as my pants were so tight I was unable to sit down with them buttoned. My black alligator boot toes were tipped with silver. I wore a white wing collared tuxedo shirt and a bolo tie with a huge turquoise stone mounted in the silver slide. The black beaver Stetson cowboy hat was banded with the same concho decoration as the belt and weighed about seven pounds. The entire clothing investment must have come up near my yearly income, but as my father would have pointed out, it was just putting lipstick on a pig.

And this is how I was dressed when I came out the front door of the

Beverly Hilton hotel. The rest of the band trash were standing around the van that was to take us to the television studio in Burbank, and even though it was night, when they saw me they all pulled out their sunglasses to shield their eyes from the blinding light that was me. Wild Bill Liberace.

You may have heard the saying, "Don't get above your raising" and it is the duty of every Southern man to jerk back to earth any of their tribe that flies too high. And I was definitely too big for the britches that I had been squeezed into. And seeing as how I could not bend at the waist, they sort of propped me up in the front passengers seat and off we went.

Now they were all dressed in basic black band trash stage wear, which is designed to not attract attention, and there was some good natured ribbing. Ol' Mark Smith says, "Do they make those pants for men?" And Macy Taylor said I looked like a troop of brownie scouts had been let loose on me with "Bedazzlers. Whole lot of love among band mates.

I laughed along with them, which sucks the sting out of a good insult, so they settled down and we rode through the crowded streets of L.A. toward the studio. Before long we came across a big grocery store and someone said we should stop and get some snacks. Or maybe it was beer, I forget which. But anyways, we pull into the parking lot and everybody decides to go in and get something, except me of course, because even on a Saturday night in L.A. I might stick out a little. So I'm leaning there all alone and I can see the store about 50 yards away, and I can see inside where the boys are checking out. Well just as they come out the doors, they run across this huge black man going in. I see them stop and enter into some conversation, and then see Ken Livsay turn and point. Right at the van. Where I am leaning. This man turns and looks my way, then they all nod, and start to grinning. The next thing I know, he's lumbering across the parking lot toward me. Did I mention he was huge? Probably six foot seven and 275 pounds. Every now and then I could catch a glimpse of his face as he came into the light. I locked the doors. Just as I got the slider locked, I heard a sharp knock on the window, and there he was. I whipped around and he was making the "roll down the window" motion, so I cracked the window an inch or two, and he peered in at me and growled, "You Garth Brooks?"

I look over his massive shoulder and see the boys slapping each other on the back and doubled over laughing like the children they were. I grin at this man and say, "No man, I ain't Garth."

And he says, "Yes you are."

And I say, "No Buddy, those guys is just pulling your leg."

And he says, "Look here Garth, my girl loves you and I want you to sign her an autograph."

Well I'm just getting ready to object, when this other fellow comes up and he says,

"Hey Ray! Who are you talking to?"

And Ray says, "Garth Brooks!"

And that other fellow turns around and hollers, "Hey! It's Garth Brooks over here in this van!"

90

And all of a sudden, the van is completely surrounded by dozens of the citizenry of L.A. All of whom had no idea what Garth Brooks looked like, because I sure as hell did not. I was starting to panic a little bit, because they were starting to shake the van and were clamoring for pictures and autographs.

"Garth! Sign my shirt!"

"I am not Garth Brooks!"

"Garth! Hold my baby!"

"Sorry Mam, but I am not who you think I am!"

"Garth!

I looked at Ray, and he glared at me, and just then I heard this soft and sultry voice say,

"What is going on here?"

And everything stopped. From the front windshield, I saw the crowd part, and there stood the most beautiful woman I have ever seen. Tall and dark, an African queen with soft brown eyes and a full, round figure clad so scantily, it left little to the imagination.

Ray says, "Hey Marie. It's Garth Brooks."

She glides over to the window, and looks in at me with those beautiful brown eyes, and purrs, "Oh Mr. Brooks, I just love the way you sing."

I looked at her, and then I looked at Ray, and then at those goof balls who were still rolling around on the ground laughing, and then back to Marie and said,

"Blame it all on my roots, I showed up in boots and ruined your black tie affair."

I signed 35 autographs, got a hug and a kiss from Marie, but graciously refused to take pictures, because I didn't want them to get home and find out they had been fooled by a faux Garth Brooks.

Work With Your Fingers

Well my Daddy got killed when I was ten
In a farming accident
We never had much, Mama took in wash
Just to meet the rent

Old Man Brown lived over the hill
And she traded out scrubbing his place
For a beat up flat top guitar
And she stuck it in my face
And she said

Work with your fingers and not your hands
Practice hard every day and find a rocking band
'Cause it's a shame when your biggest rival
Is just a fight for survival
And I know that one day son, you'll understand
Work with your fingers and not your hands

When the other guys went out on dates
I sat on my front porch swing
Picking out rhythms and playing scales
And I tried to learn to sing

Sometimes I'd get so fed up,
I'd put my guitar away
And Momma'd grab my ear and drag me back on the porch
And this is what she'd say
She'd say

Work with your fingers and not your hands
Practice hard every day and find a rocking band
What those fingers need
Is a little practice 'til they bleed
And you know of course, I'm your biggest fan
Work with your fingers and not your hands

Sometime when I'm out on the road
And I'm feeling kinda lonely and blue
I think about my Daddy and the way he died
And the pain that my Momma went through

Daddy worked hard everyday of his life
And it took him at an early age
And living on the road is killing me
But I come alive on stage
Lord I

Work with my fingers and not my hands
I practiced hard every day and got a hell of a band
'Cause it's a shame when your biggest rival
Is just a fight for survival
And tonight we'll give you everything we can
We work with our fingers and not our hands

My Hit Song

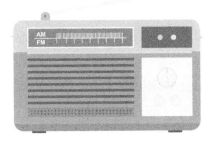

Way back in 1988 I was playing in this band called The Screaming Geezers. We were what you call a party band, five pieces, drums, bass, keyboard, rhythm and lead guitar, playing all the dance hits from whatever decade you wanted. And we had a good bit of success traveling around the South playing corporate events and fraternity parties and such, and were making a pretty good living and having lots of fun. But party bands don't get much respect. The whole idea is to play songs that everyone knows, so a great party band doesn't play any original songs. Not that the players are incapable of writing their own music, it's just that no one wants to hear it.

And we were a great party band. We had a formula that worked with any crowd we played for. It's like a roller coaster ride. First, you gotta get their attention, so you hit 'em with a rocker that everyone knows to get their blood pumping a little. The second song is designed to keep that energy going and pull them out on the dance floor. If you do it right, by the closing chorus of that second song the dance floor will be completely full. But you can't give them a break just yet, because the third song should be a party anthem that will drive them into a frenzy and when it's over they all just collapse from exhaustion. So then you can talk a bit, play a couple of slower songs to give them a chance to get a drink and catch their breath, and the whole thing starts over again.

Sometime toward the last third of the second set, you break out the sing along stuff, like "Margaritaville" and "Brown Eyed Girl."

Now everything could have just gone on the way it was and we'd all been happy, but one day we were doing a sound check before some gig and I said, "Hey, listen to this little song I wrote," and I started playing it and before long everyone jumped in and we all had a good laugh. Now I was no stranger to writing music. I had a pretty good side gig writing jingles for this ad agency which was easy and fun and made me a little extra. Y'all might have heard of a few of them, I wrote:

I got a craving for a cookie and I know what to do
Gonna grab myself a bag of Bud's Best
They're the right size, bite size, frosting in the center
Munch 'em by the fist full Buddy it's a winner
My Mom likes the quality and value, but I think they taste great, anyway!
I've been good, like I know that I should
Gonna grab myself a bag of Bud's Best, I deserve 'em
Grab myself a bag of Bud's Best!

And this one for Dale's Seasoning:

Summertime, party time, cooking on the grill
Everything's better with Dales
Thick steaks, thick chops, chicken just right
Cooking up a good time with Dales
The bull on the label says it's the best
D.A.L.E.S oh yes!
I won't cook without it, gotta shout it, everybody's talking 'bout it
Cooking up a good time with Dales — Yes sir!
Cooking up a good time with Dales

96

So one day we were in a studio recording some little jingle or another, and we finished up and had twenty minutes or so left on our time, and my drummer Todd said we ought to lay down my little song, and so we did. One take. They put it on a cassette for me and I listened to it on the way home and forgot about it. A couple of days later I got in the car and turned on the stereo and it was about half way through my song, so I listened to the rest of it and then I heard this DJ say, "That's the latest recording from Birmingham's own Screaming Geezers right here on WSGN!" And I realized my song had been playing on the radio! Just then my beeper went off and by the time I got home I had 64 messages on the answering machine. It seems that that DJ was in that recording studio after we left and the guy there had played my song for him, and he liked it and that's how that happened. And that was not the end of it either. Within a couple of weeks it had spread out to a bunch of other radio stations, and next thing I know, The Screaming Geezers are known not as a hot party band, but the band that sang that song, you know, that song on the radio.

Now I have been careful not to tell you too much about the song itself, because frankly, it's a little embarrassing. But remember, it was 1988 and I was only 27 years old, so it made a lot more sense back then, but the name of my hit song was, "Keep a Woman Like Yours from a Man Like Me." Don't judge. I'd be lying if I told you I didn't enjoy it. Every musician starts out wanting fame and fortune, but when you don't get that, you realize the real prize is making a good living doing what you love, and I was way past the "longing for fame" phase, but this little taste was sweet. I started doing radio interviews and pretty girls were hanging around and there was talk of a fan club or something.

And then one day I got this call from a record label in Los Angles California. They had heard my song and offered us a one record deal.

97

Now it wasn't a lot of money, but it did provide us with exposure on the west coast which could be big for us in the future. They took my original recording and spread it out to the radio stations out that way, and deposited a little money in an account to be used in recording our new album. And then they called and said they had us a gig set up at the Riveria Hotel and Casino in Las Vegas! It was a one week engagement in a five hundred seat showroom, with those old Vegas style red velvet booths that sat eight or ten people, and the audience was raked up from the stage, so that when you stood on the stage the audience was above you. The label was covering all our expenses which means we were paying for it, but we didn't care, we were playing Vegas baby!

I'll admit it. I might have got caught up in it a little bit. And we might have bought us some new stage clothes, but we decided to drive out instead of flying to save a little money. And it turns out it takes longer to drive from Alabama to Las Vegas than I thought, so we were running behind, but we pulled up in front of the Riveria with an hour or so to spare. And there on that big marquee, it said, "Opening Tonight! Musical Sensations, The Screaming Geezers!" All this based on one silly little novelty song I had written in about 15 minutes in the car on the way to the grocery store.

I just about busted. But there wasn't much time before we were to start, and they showed us around back where we loaded in and started setting up the equipment. Then we had just enough time to get into our new outfits, and the minute I finished tuning and plugged in my guitar, I heard the announcer say, "Ladies and Gentlemen, The Riveria Hotel and Casino is proud to present in their Las Vegas debut, The Screaming Geezers!" Now since we only had the one original song, we'd been playing our party set and working in my hit song when it felt right.

So we slammed into that first song. Todd starts banging on the drums and the shiny gold curtain starts going up and the lights are so bright we can't see a thing but we sound awesome. Years of dive bars and frat parties have the band honed to a fine point and we are rocking!

I Want to Rock and Roll All Night
Sweet Home Alabama
Saturday's Alright for Fighting!

And we hit that last power chord, and the cymbals rolled and the bass rumbled and the lead guitar wha wha-ed and the keyboard... keyboarded and I jumped up into the air to cue the stab on that last note, when according to the formula, the audience, weak kneed and sweaty, would be released from the fury of the first three songs and melt into wild applause... but. As that last note rang into silence, I clearly heard one, slow clap. And I lifted my hand to shield my eyes from the glaring lights, and there in the very center of this empty five hundred seat Las Vegas showroom, sat one very large man. And there in front of him was a plate, and on that plate was a hamburger. And with one hand he held a bottle of ketchup, and with the other he smacked the bottom. *Whap. Whap. Whap.*

Well, the rest of the week went a little better, but we never did record the album. The record company took all their money back, but we all made a little money on the gig. And the boys got some new outfits, and I got this story, so I recon we all came out about even.

(Keep a Woman Like Yours From)
A Man Like Me

Well you may think you're a Superman
Give your woman all the lovin' that she can stand
You got confidence, arrogance
You tell her that your lovin' is heaven sent
But I got some advice that I'll give you for free
Keep a woman like yours from a man like me

Now you're sitting there in that easy chair
With your feet propped up and without a care
Your woman's out with that red dress on
So tired of being at home alone
You gotta give her all your lovin' from A to Z
To keep a woman like yours from a man like me

'Cause I'll hold her, stroke her,
Tell her all the things that you should have told her
Maybe, you'll see
That you can learn a lot of things from a man like me

Well somewhere there's a band that's playing it hot
And there's a woman that a aching for what I got
And you're at home alone with that football game
Lord have mercy, who's the one to blame
You better wake up son and turn off the TV
To keep a woman like yours from a man like me

Rusty McGraw the Bird Dog

When I was a boy more than anything else in the whole wide world, I wanted me a dog. So I did what any eight year old boy would do, I begged and pleaded and whined and promised until one day my Daddy came home with a great big box from the McGraw Apple Orchard, and when I opened it up out jumped the cutest little rust colored retriever pup you ever saw. I named him Rusty McGraw. Now Rusty McGraw was a bird dog. And I say that not because of his ability to retrieve game, but because that dog could fly.

Rusty McGraw was a bird dog and he could jump so high
Clear up over the backyard fence and spit in an eagle's eye
Other dogs might be stronger or the first to fetch the toy
But something about the air up there filled his heart with joy
He was born to fly

Old Rusty was the jumpinest dog you ever saw. When he was just a pup no more than a foot tall, he could jump up on the table and if you wern't looking, he'd lick all the milk right out of your cereal. And no ice cream cone could be held so high that Rusty couldn't get his self a lick. And in the morning, when you'd be all snuggled in the covers trying to get an extra five minutes of sleep, Rusty would jump up on the bed and light soft as a feather – tugging on those blankets, wagging and a barking – get up you lazy bones!

Rusty McGraw the bird dog weren't one to laze around
He gave every jump his best and rested coming down
His nose was like an airfoil, hind legs like steel springs
And when you saw that dog take off, you'd swear that he had wings
He was born to fly

On the next street over but one, there lived a pure bred Standard Poodle named Fifi. OK. I just made that up. I don't really know what her name was, but she sure looked like a Fifi. Anyways her people took great stock in her blood line and she'd given birth to several expensive litters of pure bred standard poodle pups. And they kept her inside most of the time but every now and again they would let her run around in their backyard which was surrounded by an eight foot tall wooden fence. And then one day Rusty come along. That's why we have Labradoodles.

Old Rusty McGraw was a bird dog of extraordinary power
He jumped over the Golden Gate and the tip of the Eiffel Tower
With every record that he broke he'd bark out happily
Cause it was in his nature to defy gravity
He was born to fly

Being a blessed child, I never actually had a pet that passed away on me. They just took positions with other families. My frogs moved to France. My fish went from tank to toilet to the sea. Cat missing? There's a new king in Katmandu. And as for Rusty....

One happy day the strangest thing did happen to that pup
He jumped off the boat dock and kept on going up
And sometimes on a moon lit night if you look up in the sky
You might see that bird dog as he passes by
He was born to fly
He was born to fly

Second Chance

In September of 2021, I had a heart attack. I'll spare you the details but heart attacks hurt. I had what they call a widow maker, and got a ride in a helicopter to the UT Medical Center in Knoxville, where they ripped off my pants, ran a tube from my stem to my sternum, placed a couple of stents in my arteries and… I lived. I never thought I was going to die, but I did think, "This is how people die."

After you have had a heart attack and you get over the "I'm alive" part, you may experience some feelings of, well, guilt. You see, except for the ratty pajamas you are wearing, you look just fine. And because there is blood flowing freely through your entire system, you feel better than you have in quite a while. All of a sudden you can breathe. But even though you feel fine, them doctors pretty much insist you take a little time off.

When my wife went back to work, I had a lot of time alone. Just me and the cats. Now nobody is mad at you but it feels like they make you take time off just so you can think about what you have done and face up to whatever it was got you there. And cats can be so judgmental.

So my wife I got me a pen and a little notebook so I could reflect on my life in longhand. She said, "Write down everything that comes to mind." So at the top of the page I wrote, "How did I get here?"

And after an hour or so of staring at a blank page I decided to take a little break. So I wrote the word "Break." And then I thought, "break" That's a funny word. And I started writing.

The word "break" has a whole bunch of meanings. As a verb, it means to separate in to pieces. It can also mean interrupt, you can take a break, and stop doing whatever it is you were doing and have a Kit Kat.

It means you fail to observe the law, and if while you are in jail they don't break your spirit, you may devise a plan to break out, soon after which the news of your escape would break. The weather can break, waves break and day breaks all the time. And you can break a heart, figuratively and literally.

As a noun, it can mean a interruption in continuity, or a pause in activity. Let's take a break.

It can mean a gap — a break in traffic, and it can mean to run away, make a break for it. You can break in, break out, break up, break down, break free and break your back in the process. You can get a break, a special advantage that you may or may not deserve. Some guys get all the breaks.

And taking liberties with the English language, we can change the spelling from eak to ake and put your foot on the noun brake and verb brake to a complete stop.

A break may or may not cover a specific period of time. A sabbatical is a break that may last a year. A vacation break, a couple of weeks. You get two days a week for a work break, an hour for your lunch break and ten minutes here and there for bathroom and or mental health breaks.

Take as many as you need.

No matter the length of your break, it must come to an end. But the end of every break is a new beginning. It doesn't matter if it's a long break or just a short pause, you have an opportunity to make a change. It's a second chance to change your mind and try and get it right.

A few years back I thought I might like to make a little turn in my professional life. Not a huge jump, but perhaps find a different market to share my skill set. But just as I started figuring it out, Covid hit and there wasn't much of a way to move forward and then I got busy with other things, and then I had the heart attack and everything just stopped.

I used my forced break to write more. More stories, more songs. Take the opportunity to get what I have inside me, out. So here I am.

Sometimes it seems like you just can't catch a break. And sometimes, the good Lord slams on the brakes, makes you take a break, and it turns out to be just the break you need.

The Great Pancake Challenge of 1968

Dixie Dawson owned and operated the City Cafe in Northport, Alabama. The cafe was open from 5:30am until 2pm Monday through Saturday, and unlike any other cafe you ever been to in your entire lifetime, there were no menus. You simply ate whatever Dixie was making that day, and you were always glad to, 'cause it was always good. At lunch it was what we call a meat and three, might be pork chops with green beans, corn on the cob and fried potatoes and banana pudding, or hamburger steak with gravy, mashed potatoes, fried okra with lemon pound cake. Didn't matter. It was good. Now breakfast was always the same, scrambled eggs, bacon and sausage, hash browns, biscuits and gravy and what were known far and wide as the best pancakes in the whole wide world.

The cafe was always packed with every kind of person imaginable, and you'd have to sit wherever there was an empty seat and if you were really lucky you might pull up a chair at the table of Pete Herman and Sam Maxwell. Pete and Sam held the center table every day that cafe was open from 8:30 until noon, eating two meals without giving up their seats. And everyone knew that that was their table. I've seen four big burly working men get up and finish breakfast standing when Pete and Sam came in.

Now while Pete and Sam were the best of friends, they never actually agreed on anything. Pete was an Auburn man, Sam, Alabama. Pete a republican, Sam a yellow dog democrat. Pete liked Ginger, Sam, Mary Ann. They'd sit and argue about this and that, none of which had any consequence at all, until one day, they began a quarrel that would change that little town forever.

It all began innocently enough. One Saturday morning Pete mentioned that the pancakes were particularly good that day, and Sam said he thought they were better the day before, and that led to a discussion about which one was more qualified to critique pancakes in general, based upon the number of pancakes consumed in their respective histories, and that led to a even more heated discussion regarding which could eat the most pancakes at one sitting. And thus the Great Pancake Challenge of 1968 was born.

They decided the competition would take place the following Monday morning, so that each could prepare for the contest. Now a day and a half is more than enough time for word to spread like wildfire throughout a small town, with some folks getting behind Sam, and others behind Pete. And before the end of the day, the fellows at the barber shop were laying down fifty cent bets on one or the other, and the next morning, the Methodist preacher had changed his sermon, which was to be on the evils of alcohol, to the evils of gambling.

By the time the appointed hour came, the entire town was crammed into Dixie's and she had to send Raymond over to the Piggly Wiggly to get more coffee. Sam came in first, dressed in his dough boy uniform from the "war to end all wars" and a great cheer rose up from his supporters. Then Pete arrived in his over-alls and old cardigan, and an equally raucous cheer went up. The crowd closed in tight as the two old friends sat down across the table from one another, glaring over a pile of pancakes big enough to feed the city of Atlanta. They each started with a short stack, two pancakes each, dripping in butter and Golden Eagle table syrup, which they dispatched in short order. And then they upped the stakes with a stack of three each, then four. By the time they began the next round, beads of sweat were forming on Pete's brow, and little dried drops of corn sugar congealed on Sam's mustache. The crowd, which had remained fairly quiet, could see each of them slowing down a bit and began to uneasily encourage their champion on. Total – 13 pancakes.

They both stopped syruping the cakes, and went to dry eating. The following round they put down their forks and began eating one at a time by hand. Total : 17 cakes. 18 cakes. The crowd was losing their collective mind, chanting in unison and sending up great roars as a pancake disappeared down their champs gullet. Time slowed to a crawl and Sam and Pete struggled to reach for one more pancake. 22 pancakes, 23 pancakes. After the 24th cake, the two old friends seemed to forget what they were arguing about in the first place and gratefully and graciously agreed that two dozen seemed to be a good place to stop and to the chagrin of the barbershop underworld, settled for a tie. But as the gamblers went to retrieve their stakes, they found they had lost their money, because there was one man who covered each and every bet on that tie. The Methodist preacher collected $28.00 and Pete and Sam remained best friends, and as far as I know they are still meeting at Dixie's everyday.

Oh, and as for changing that little town forever? I might have exaggerated that a bit.

Faith of Steel

Six days Grandpa worked the mine
On Sunday preached the word divine
He worked like hell in that dark hole
Then prayed to save the miner's soul
Coal man, iron will, faith of steel.

He was born in a Central Alabama coal mining town
Midst the dust and the mud and the rocks
Where the only way in is to be born there
And the only way out is a box

And though his hands were coal stained,
he'd been taught to read by King James
Raised up on a foundation of faith, family,
service to your fellow man
With conviction that the next life awaiting
was better than the life at hand
Better than the poverty, better than the hunger,
and free to all who choose it
He'd been born with the gift of persuasion,
and called by his God to use it

So just as the blue black coal
that he pulled from that damp dark earth
would be transformed by fire,
And in turn, transform the cold and the night,
He used his words to transform men,
and bring them from darkness to light

And in that sacred Sunday hour
his words carried so much power
They touched the hearts and the minds of the unsaved
And they turned their backs on their wicked ways
and were free
He brought so many of the lost
to the foot of the Savior's cross
that The Prince of Darkness himself took note
And in the bowels of purgatory
he called out the head devil of that territory
In their weekly staff meeting
"I see from this latest report" the Devil said with a frown,
"You're losing souls on that mountain,
what's dragging your numbers down?"

"Oh Great Satan!" that under devil cried,
"It's that coal mining preacher, he's turning the tide,
We've lost gossips and haters, liars and traitors,
gamblers and cheaters and wife beaters,
We've lost politicians, musicians,
Morticians and beauticians,
rogues and cads and dead beat dads,
If we don't put a stop this shitz
We just might lose the hypocrites."

The Devil sighs and rolls his eyes,
it's hard to get good help these days
Just for fun, he'll take this one,
He'd show these rookies how it's done.

Well Sir, the meeting room was completely packed,
so in his disguise he stood way in the back
And listened as Grandpa spun his Holy spell,
the joy of heaven, the horror of hell
And his frustration grew worse and worse
with every call, with every verse,
"Come home! Come home! Ye who are weary, come home!"

And to their knees, the weary dropped,
And Satan knew, this must be stopped!
So as Grandpa sang his final plea,
he threw off his cloak, stepped into the aisle, revealed himself
And cried out, "Coal man! What about me?"

For those of you that have never actually seen the face of evil,
picture this:

Red and scaly, eight feet tall
With horns and a pitch fork and a long tail, but that ain't all
He looks like fear and doubt,
worry and greed and jealousy and hate
He looks like "I'm not good enough"
"You're not good enough" "I am better than you"
Racism, sexism, politics the lowest of the low
In short, he looks like ego

And he's hard to look at, like truth,
or staring at a mirror so clear it reveals your every flaw
So the congregation turned their eyes away,
ashamed of what they saw

The devil stalked down the aisle toward the alter of God,
and the stench of brimstone filled the air
And with a cloven hoof he drew a line,
and made his challenge there
"Coal man bow down at my feet,
or stand behind the words you preach!"

But the little man that Old Scratch faced,
was a titan of courage, a giant of faith
Purified in the blast furnace called life in the Alabama mud
Coal dust in his lungs, iron in his blood
Carbonized by the strength of his will
And when your doubt turns to slag, your faith turns to steel
What makes you tick, what makes you go
Is not what you believe, it's what you know

And the words of God that banned his fear
Came straight to his heart, rang loud and clear
Just as God speaks to you and me if only we could hear
His greatest promise

Be not afraid
For I am with you

always.

Even unto the end of time,
even through your darkest night
When your family turns their back
Through addiction, and pain, and want and lack
I am there through your greatest fears
And even if Satan himself appears,
Be not afraid, I am with you always

And no one there believed their eyes,
and even Ol' Lucifer was surprised,
When Grandpa let out a mighty roar,
jumped the alter, lit on the floor
And the right hand of God came up from the ground
Square to his jaw and spun him around
And Grandpa kicked that tail so hard
He flew down the aisle and out in the yard,
with Grandpa close behind

They kicked and hit and punched and bit
and the devil got the worst of it
He lost his pitchfork back in the church, a few teeth along the way
His horns were bent, his eyes swelled shut, the picture of Hell to pay
By the time the fight was through, Grandpa gave that devil his due
Grabbed his tail and swung him round,
and threw him high and as he came down
The earth below him opened wide
and flames shot up as he fell inside

And just like that, he was gone.

The ass whipping that the devil took,
ain't a sermon from the holy book
But when the battle was won all the witness' knew
It ain't the size of the demon you face
It's the size of the God in you

Now on that mountain in the wood
There's a clearing where that church once stood
And a hole that they could never fill
Where Satan met a faith of steel
Coal man, iron will, faith of steel

Chapter Five

Odds and Ends

Odds and Ends
or
Chop Suey

Just when I thought that I was finished with my book, I realized I had a few things that didn't really fit anywhere in the chapters. But I wanted to put them in somewhere so I would have them printed in what will most likely be my only book. Your indulgence is appreciated.

This first bit is a poem I wrote for a contest held by the Vitamin Water company. There was a video with some great music and a professional voice over featuring yours truly. First prize was $100,000.00. I did not win. Boo. But it was an attempt to actually say something important, and I'd like to tell you I took my own advice, but…
Oh well.

The next piece is my tribute to Paula Deen. It plays everyday at the Lumberjack Feud. I really like Paula, she's a true Southern Lady and I'm trying to trick her into cooking something for me.

And finally, there are a few poems that just didn't seem to fit anywhere else, but I hope you like them!

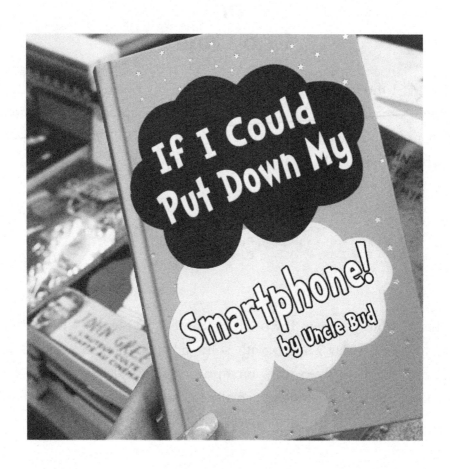

If I could put down my Smartphone
Oh! What a world would be seen!
'Cause the world's so much wider,
And bolder and brighter
Than the world on my
Smartphone screen.

First, I would learn how to listen
To the people I encounter each day
Without all the scrolling
And internet trolling
I might find they've got
Something to say!

Without all my Snapchat filters,
To enhance this face that I hide
I'd be forced to reveal
The face that is real
And the person
That's waiting inside

I'd become a man of rare courage,
And bravely face all my fears
Swim with a shark, go into the dark,
Change that light bulb,
That's been burned out
A couple of years.

If I could put down my Smartphone,
I'd have extra time to create
I'd cure cancer one morning and
Reverse global warming
Before we find out it's too late.

Homelessness? Solved.
Poverty? Fixed.
All the garbage plucked
Out the ocean!
My simple solution
To reduce air pollution?
Perfecting perpetual motion.

I'd address a joint session of Congress,
And bring them together
'Cross the aisle
Then turn my attention
To easing world tension
By sharing a Coke and a smile

I could learn the language of animals,
The yak, the baboon and the otter
We'd sit 'neath a tree,
Discuss philosophy
While sipping on Vitamin Water.

If I could put down my
Smartphone, here's a few
Other things I would do,
Learn to skate, Lose some
Weight, and consider
Adopting a new point of view.

Finish a crossword puzzle
Learn how to sneeze and not blink
Learn to cook, write a book,
Play the banjo,
And not give a hoot what folks think.

In my backyard, I'd build
A huge rocket and blast
Off for Mars or for Venus
And there all alone,
Without my Smartphone
I'd find out the smarter between us!

And after a year with no Smartphone
I might take a peek at my wall
Read all the boasting and
Mindless meme posting and
Find I've missed nothing at all!

And if I win this
Contest or not,
I think I'll give it a shot!

Hey Y'all It's Paula!

I know a gal that's sweet as honey it's Paula Deen
Smart as Grandpa, twice as funny it's Paula Deen
Lays a table just like Nanna it's Paula Deen
That lady from Sweet Home Savannah, It's Paula Deen

Hey Y'all it's Paula, it's Paula Deen
Hey Y'all it's Paula, it's Paula Deen

Come gather round her family table it's Paula Deen
And wait for grace if you are able it's Paula Deen
Her fried chicken drives me crazy it's Paula Deen
I love her biscuits sopped in gravy it's Paula Deen

Hey Y'all it's Paula, it's Paula Deen
Hey Y'all it's Paula, it's Paula Deen

There's butter in that recipe, it's Paula Deen
It clarifies her legacy yeah, it's Paula Deen
Southern charm that never misses it's Paula Deen
She sends to you love and best dishes it's Paula Deen

Hey Y'all it's Paula, it's Paula Deen
Hey Y'all it's Paula, it's Paula Deen

Hey Y'all it's Paula, it's Paula Deen
Hey Y'all it's Paula, it's Paula Deen

Piece of Cake

It was early Saturday morning
when she took her coat and hat
And stood there in the doorway
with a grin reminding me that

I had agreed, (never you mind
how I was coerced to agree)
To watch our three-year-old niece
while the women folk
went on a shopping spree

And now the day was here,
but I wasn't too upset
After all, we have chickens to feed
and horses to ride
and dogs and cats to pet

And I remember,
when I was a boy
I'd rather play with critters
than any store-bought toy

So it was with confidence
I greeted them at the door
Molly held her dolly
and stared up from the floor

127

She smiled so sweetly from amongst
a blonde head full of curls
And suddenly it dawned on me…
she's not a rough and tumble boy,
she's a baby girl

Maybe she won't want to ride
or toss out chicken feed
And fear crept in; I knew nothing about
what a little girl might need

But I shook it off, heck;
I'd find us things to do
After all, I'm a clever man,
and it's only an hour or two

She's so cute and sweet
we'll find some games to play
But the horror began before her mother
was half a mile away!

It started innocently enough,
could she have a little snack?
But she pulled the curtains off the window
the minute I turned my back!

And before I came from the kitchen
with her cookies and her juice
She emptied thirteen house plants
and turned our goldfish loose!

As I was scooping those flopping fish
from the floor back to the water
I became convinced my sister-in-law
was raising the devil's daughter

She bounced up and down like a rubber ball
all around the house
And I ran around behind her picking up,
and dog cussin' my loving spouse

But all good things must come to an end,
and thankfully, so did this
The juice wore off and she went down
in a sugar induced coma of bliss

I still had my chores to do,
so I left her curled up on the floor
In front of a Barney video
with Pedro, our Labrador

When I got finished with all my work
and came back to the house
I took off my shoes at the kitchen door
and snuck in quiet as a mouse

I tip-toed down the hallway,
whispering the apostle's creed
To protect myself from awakening
the blonde haired demon-seed

But Molly and the lab were still curled up,
and it couldn't be much finer
So I kicked off my boots and lay my aching body
down in the recliner

Next thing I knew I heard the front door open
and started up, but felt heavy in my chest
And realized Molly had climbed up on me
when I'd laid down for my rest

I saw the flash of the camera,
and heard the women aw and coo
They flitted about and scooped Molly up,
and out the door they flew

"I don't believe it" said my wife.
I lay there nearly dead.
But I just grinned and closed my eyes.
"Piece of cake," is all I said.

The Twenties

In '29 it hit the fan, jobs were scarce for every man
And just to feed a family, took a lot from a man like me
We stood in line and towed the rope,
and tried to hang on to a little hope
'Cause on the radio Hoover said there's better days ahead

But the Thirties came and the shelves were bare,
God wouldn't hear our prayer
Tryin' to save our family home, I felt so all alone
The banks shut down and lost their riches,
serves them right, them sons of bitches
We hung onto the government lies, and somehow we survive

Roosevelt came with his New Deal promising our land to heal
And every dollar that they spent tied us to the government
But it gave us jobs, gave us a chance
to wake up from that awful trance
And from our slumber we began to live again like men

And then the 40's brought us war, plows pounded into swords
Gave our children hand grenades, and ticker tape parades
But the cost of every battle won,
was the life of some poor mother's son
And the blood we shed we justify and somehow we survive

In every time there's bad, there's good, there's tragedies misunderstood
We try to learn from past mistakes, but sometimes it's a waste
'Cause the hardest times make tougher men,
tougher times make better friends
And the blessing right before our eyes, is together we survive

Attachment

I threw my saddle in the back of his truck and thanked him for the ride,
I'd had Old Jenny eleven years, but now, my mustang had died
She'd seemed just fine, a few miles back when we left Mr. Johnson's store
But then she stalled, then completely quit, and I knew she couldn't go no more

So I just sat down beside her and lit a cigarette,
And thought of all the good times we'd had and swore I'd never forget
Her many contributions to the mile-stones in my life
We'd been out for a ride when Betty Sue agreed to be my wife

And she was there when I bought the ranch and when Little Bill was born
And now all I could do was sit and wait for Gabriel to blow his horn
Then I saw old Pete a' coming across the flat and dusty land
We had but a few more minutes alone, so I nuzzled her with my hand

"You've been a good friend" I said aloud, but I couldn't say the part
But I think she heard the symphony that swelled within my heart
Now a smaller man might be ashamed but I'm quite proud to say
That before Old Pete got to where we sat, I'd brushed a tear away

So I climbed in the cab in silence, and Pete stared straight ahead
Out of respect, I recon, 'cause he could see that she was dead
Finally, some words came, and Pete gently punched my arm
She'd have her final resting place on the backside of the barn

And we laughed a bit to ease the pain, it's funny how much you feel
For the passing of your mustang, even though it's just a hunk of steel
And the radio just barely worked, and the dash was dried and cracked
But there's no telling what I'd give, if I could have her back

"This will pass" I thought out loud and Pete asked me if I knew
What I was going to do next, I said, "I'm thinking Suburu."

Prologue

I am the kind of person who likes to work on things. Often this leads to never actually finishing anything. But I guess completing this book is more important than tinkering around with it for a few more years. So I am going to stop.

If you saw your name in one of the stories and were offended, it was another Joe or Dolphus I was referring to, so get over it. If it made you laugh, it was you I was talking about.

I hope you found something in here to amuse you or maybe even make you ponder a bit. Like I said in the Forward, it was all written for me to tell it out loud, but since we're not together, I reckon this book is about the best I can do. Maybe we'll see each other and I'll tell you one. And I just might be convinced to play the banjo. We'll see.

Anyways, I had fun writing all this, so at least there's that. Y'all be good to one another and I hope to hug your neck real soon.

Uncle Bud

Made in the USA
Columbia, SC
12 August 2024

39925989R00085